To Mitch,

A great friend,
Skydiver, patriot and
brother in Christ.

Nick

Book Reviews

The Lynx is a powerful and inspirational story of courage and commitment to freedom. It is also a fascinating view of the story of Cuba during the Cold War. I highly recommend it!

—Admiral James Stavridis, USN (Ret.) Commander, U.S. Southern Command 2006-2009. Supreme Allied Commander, NATO 2009-2011. Author of "*The Accidental Admiral and Destroyer Captain.*"

The Lynx is the harrowing account of a man's extraordinary quest for freedom in the face of heart-pounding, life threatening odds. Exciting, inspirational, and replete with international intrigue, Nick's unforgettable story has all of the ingredients of a John LeCarre novel, except for one critical aspect: all of the action, all of the people, and all of the circumstances are real. Through his own patience, innovation, and sheer competence, Nick manage single- handedly to turn all other Cold War defection stories on their head. If you want to truly appreciate your freedom-or just need to be reminded from time to time

—The Lynx is a very, very good place to start.

—John Fenzel, "*The Sterling Forest*" (Breathe Press, 2016), "*The Lazarus Covenant*" (Breathe Press, 2009).

John Fenzel is a retired Senior Special Forces officer who served on our nation's battlefields throughout Europe and the Middle East. He served on the personal staffs of the Secretary of Defense, Army Chief of Staff, and the Vice President of the United States. Following the Cold War, he led the first U.S. deployments to the Baltic States.

---

*I first met the author and protagonist at the Pan American Parachute Games in Peru, 1975. In **The Lynx**, Nick paints his amazing story with the authority of a personal witness to one of the most critical stages of Cuban communism, and of his extraordinary struggle for freedom. Against all odds, Lince became a world-class parachutist with the sole purpose of escaping from the prison island—a mighty demonstration of the unbreakable spirit of human survival. It is an absolutely real and exciting story. A must read.*

—Tomás Dánil Berriolo, President of the Pan American Parachuting Federation, 1972-1980. Recipient of the highly distinguished *"Paul Tissandier"* Diploma by the Fédération Aéronautique Internationale.

VICTOR "NICK" NICKOLICH

A TRUE STORY OF INTRIGUE, DECEIT, AND TRIUMPH IN
THE MIDST OF THE COLD WAR

Shreiber Press

The Lynx

Copyright © 2016 by Victor Nickolich.

Published in the United States of America ISBN: 978-0-9979799-3-0
Library of Congress Control Number: 2016914392
The Lynx—Nickolich, Victor —Ed. I. Title

1. Biography & Autobiography / Personal Memoirs

2. Biography & Autobiography / Political

3. History / Cuba-20th Century First Edition

For my wonderful children, Stana and Lucas,
whom I love and admire more than
they will ever know. And, for my wife, Loes,
who makes everything possible.

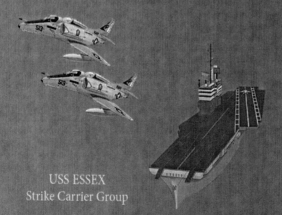

FLORIDA STRAITS

B26 Invaders

La Palma Cayo la Rosa La Habana
San Cristobal   San Nicolas   Varadero
Pinar del Rio   Matanzas

Sea Fury

2506 Brigade
Airborne Troops

Zapata Peninsula

New Gerona   Bay of Pigs

Isle of Pines   Playa Larga   Cienfuegos   Escambra

Bay of Pigs Invasion
April 17, 1961

Trinidad

CARIBBEAN SEA

USS ESSEX
Strike Carrier Group

FLORIDA STRAITS

Mountains

ara

Ciego de Avila

Camaguey

Las Tunas

Holguin

CUBANA Vicker's
Viscount Crash Site

Bahia de Nipe

Bayamo   Charco Redondo   Moa

Sierra del Cristal

Sierra Maestra

Santiago de   Guantanamo
Cuba

BEECHCRAFT
BONANZA

CAYMAN TRENCH

Prologue

A thick haze had engulfed the airfield overnight. In spite of the near zero visibility, the runner managed to keep a steady pace on the two kilometer stretch of uneven trail that bordered the paved runway. He had run the footpath many times before and knew every dip and bump of the terrain.

The man found solace in jogging alone at dawn. It was the quietest time of the day when the only sounds heard were that of his own breathing, and his shoes crushing the dew-covered grass. The open spaces brought clarity to his thoughts and allowed him to daydream undisturbed.

That tranquility, however, was ephemeral. Within minutes, the airfield would bustle once again with the sights and sounds of an active crop duster base, which doubled as a training center for the national parachute team. Shortly after dawn, the Russian AN-2 crop dusters would start taking off to spray the nearby sugar cane fields. By the time the last duster got off the ground, another plane would move to the tarmac to pick-up the first load of skydivers.

Nick sprinted the last fifty yards and headed for the barracks. He had a few minutes left in which to shower, grab his parachute, and make a dash for the AN-2. The sunlight he had seen filtering through the fog on the horizon promised another perfect day ahead.

Nonetheless, sometimes life takes unexpected turns. While the skydiver was ready in mind and body for a full day of training, destiny had reserved a very different story for him.

Part I

THE ENIGMA

THE LYNX

Chapter 1

Decision is a risk rooted in the courage of being free.
— *Paul Tillich*

In the summer of 1977, an elite group of skydivers sojourned at the San Nicolas airfield to train for the Pan American Parachuting Championships. Their coach was Anatoli *Tolia* Yurenkov, a former U.S.S.R. champion and a member of a Spetsnaz airborne unit in the Soviet Republic of Ukraine. Tolia was burly, rough around the edges and hardly spoke any Spanish, but proved to be a most talented instructor. At the end of the four-month-long camp, he had qualified the Cuban team as a favorite to win the gold in Mexico.

The fog cleared shortly after eight, revealing a seamless blue sky and a light breeze that blew in from the west. Before noon, all four team members had scored five perfect dead center landings on the target—a pattern that had repeated itself for the past few weeks. With only six days to go, the team was set for an almost certain victory. In retrospect, every night spent away from home, every parachute repacked under the scorching sun and every crash landing on the ten-centimeter disc had proven worth their while.

This would be Cuba's second appearance at the Pan Americans, an event held every two years and one of its kind on the continent. Several military and civilian parachute teams would convene once again to put their skills to the test against one another. But as in the last few meets, the team to beat would be the U.S. Army Golden Knights, the undefeated Pan American champions.

The clock was ticking for the day the United States and Cuba would face off again, this time in the skies over Tequesquitengo. Two years earlier, in Peru, the USA had defeated Cuba in the team accuracy event by a small margin of points. Now the Cubans would have another chance to challenge the Golden Knights and reverse the results from Peru.

Nick repacked his Russian UT-15 parachute, grabbed a sandwich at the cafeteria and headed to the barracks for a quick nap. Once again, his thoughts started drifting off to a seemingly distant past. Seven years had passed by since the day he set out to become a skydiver with the sole purpose of taking flight from the prison island. Now an accomplished competitor and three-time member of the Cuban national team, he had not wavered from his determination to escape.

Seven years later, he thought. He had read somewhere that seven was indeed the number of divine perfection. To him, it was now or never.

The skydiver was about to doze off when he noticed Tolia storming in through the barrack door. The Ukrainian halted momentarily, adjusted his vision to the darkness, and then headed straight toward his bunk. Thick drops of sweat could be seen dripping down his chiseled face.

"Nick, *pochemu ti niet* Mexico—why are you not going to Mexico? Are you a hooligan?"

"A hooligan? Only when I'm asleep," Nick joked, taken aback by Tolia's impromptu foray.

"Lince, the coach is dead serious," said Kymbe, one of his teammates. Just like the pilots, most jumpers were given call signs. Nick's was Lince—Spanish for Lynx.

"I just had a talk with Melo. He told me that you are in trouble with the police and that you are no longer part of the national team. What have you done?"

"Tolia, that's not true. Somebody has made a mistake."

"Unfortunately, your replacement has already been named. Raul will take your slot and Enrique will go as the team alternate. My problem is that neither man has the skills to compete in Mexico. The team's chances to make it to the podium at the Pan Americans are now zero—*nil*."

It took a few seconds for Tolia's words to sink in. The only police agency that could have ordered his removal from the team was the Directorate of State Security—the feared DSE. Had the DSE discovered that he intended to defect in Mexico? If that was the case, how in the world did they find out?

Three days earlier, the skydivers had a closed-door meeting with Lieutenant Tony Angulo, the Cuban intelligence officer in charge of internal security. Angulo had given them the political lecture that had preceded all their previous trips overseas. As in previous occasions, the officer had them sign a document with the rules of engagement—everything they were not supposed to do, or say while in Mexico. The regime would use that paper against them if there were any violations of the rules.

However, nothing at the meeting raised a flag that he could in trouble with the DSE. Whatever prompted his sudden separation from the team had happened within the past twenty-four to forty-eight hours.

The skydiver excused himself to Tolia and stepped out of the barracks. He needed some fresh air and have a talk with Melo. The man who broke the news to the coach should be able to shed some light on the issue that had just turned his life upside down.

Lince stormed into the airport's operations office without knocking. A startled Melo took his feet off his desk and sat up straight. The man had been in a crop duster accident a few years earlier and lost partial use of one leg. Unable to pass the physical and re-qualify as a pilot, Melo was now in charge of the crop dusters and the skydiving operations at San Nicolas. He was taller than the average Cuban—lean, witty, and sported a large mustache that gave him a jocular appearance.

"Melo, what's going on? Tolia just told me that I am no longer part of the team. I don't appreciate hearing the bad news at second hand."

It was not up to me. Luciano called me earlier today and told me to replace you with Raul, and to tell the Ukrainian right away. Tolia became overly excited after hearing the news. For a second I thought he was going to punch me in the face. He seems to be very fond of you. I feel awful."

"Somebody messed up big time. This whole issue did not just create a problem for me alone. It has trashed all chances for Cuba to win a medal in Mexico. Is the State Security behind this mess?"

Melo nodded. "It has to be them. Luciano wants you to pack all your stuff and meet him at the club headquarters this afternoon. He will tell you everything."

"The shuttle bus doesn't leave until later in the evening. How am I supposed to get there on time?"

"No worries. I have already taken care of that. An inspector from the Civil Aeronautics Institute is leaving for Havana in the next half hour or so. He will give you a ride."

"I will be ready in five minutes. Maybe I'll see you again when I get out of the slammer."

"Good luck to you. Let me know your new address. I would like to send you cigarettes," he joked.

Back at the barracks, Lince emptied his locker under the baffled stare of his teammates.

"It's the State Security," Lince told them. "I don't know what they have on me now, but I'm not going down without a fight. Don't count me out yet."

"Give them hell, partner. We need you in Mexico," stammered Kymbe.

The realization that the State Security was involved made Kymbe quiver. The DSE was the highest authority in the land, second only to the Castro brothers and a handful of people in the Communist Party. The team's dreams of defeating the Golden Knights in Mexico had just gone up in smoke.

The red Lada was waiting at the far end of the parking lot with its engine running. As Lince got near the car, he noticed the driver reaching over to open the passenger door.

"Lince?" the man asked.

"That's me"

"My name is Marcos. I will give you a ride to the city. Please get in."

"Thank you."

"Make yourself comfortable. We should be in Havana in less than an hour."

Melo had told him the driver worked for the Civil Aeronautics Institute. However, judging from the bulge on the back of his shirt, Marcos was carrying a gun. The only people allowed to carry concealed weapons in Cuba were the undercover agents from the Ministry of Interior. Melo had not told him the whole story.

Lince suspected that Marcos was a DSE agent dispatched to San Nicolas to take him back to Havana, make notes of everything he said and study his reactions. He decided not to talk about his problem unless his driver asked him. Marcos did not. The man spent the entire drive talking about the ongoing baseball season and switching stations on the Lada's scratchy radio.

The veil of secrecy shrouding his hasty send-off was unnerving. He took his logbook out of his backpack and started jotting down the jumps he made that morning. He needed some time by himself to think and figure out the reason for his predicament. If he could guess the answer maybe he could prepare for his defense before he came face to face with Luciano.

His thoughts transported him back to the fall of 1976, the fateful day when two Canadian skydivers—Gabriel and Derek—showed up unannounced in Cuba. Lince was fluent in English and the club director asked him to take the men skydiving to San Nicolas. He was also told not to lose sight of them. The DSE wanted to know what those guys were up to.

After the jumps, Lince invited the Canadians to his home for dinner. The men had expressed their interest in meeting Lince's parents when they learned that his father, Victor Daniels Nickolich, was an American engineer who had lived on the island for forty-five years.

That night, Lince opened up to the Canadians. He told Gabriel and Derek about his long disagreement with Castro's regime and of his intentions to escape during the next competition abroad. He reasoned that his newly made friends might have some ideas on how to accomplish that goal.

Lince's frankness prompted Gabriel to make a surprising revelation of his own. He told Lince that he had recently met an American jumper who worked as an aide to Henry Kissinger, the outgoing U.S. Secretary of State. Upon his return to Canada, he could call his friend in D.C. and tell him about Lince's dilemma. If the Americans knew of his intentions ahead of time, they might help him break through the Cuban security in Mexico and so ultimately help him gain his freedom. The U.S. State Department would never turn their back on one of their own, so they concurred.

However, if the secret leaked and the Cubans were to find out, he would be arrested and sent to rot in prison for the rest of his life. In spite of the risks involved, Lince gave the green light to Gabriel to contact his friend in Washington. He might not have a similar opportunity ever again. That night, Lince wrote a letter to his sister in the United States, which Derek promised to mail for him from Vancouver.

Six months later, an unexpected storm took shape ninety miles north of Cuba. Without a warning, President Jimmy Carter ordered the United States government to initiate the process of restoring the long broken diplomatic ties with the regime of Fidel Castro.

While the sudden news came as a shock to many people in Cuba, they were particularly disturbing to Lince. He wondered if he had made a mistake by sharing his secret with the Americans that far ahead of time. In hindsight, he decided that he should have waited until after he arrived in Mexico to make contact with the U.S. officials. Now it was too late to change anything.

"Are you okay?" asked Marcos. Apparently, the man had noticed his deep state of introspection. Lince still had the pen in his hand, but was no longer writing.

"I'm fine. I'm just tired from today's training."

Marcos glanced back at him from the corner of his eye and gave a nod. His face reminded Lince of a hawk.

As the Russian-built sedan sped toward Havana, the man known as Lince felt a sudden chill running down his spine. Could it be possible that the same people he sought help from had double-crossed him? The likelihood that someone at the U.S. State Department had cozied up to the Cubans and leaked his intentions to defect suddenly became a daunting reality. He braced himself for the worst.

Chapter 2

The first duty of a man is to think for himself.
— *José Martí*

Nick was a quiet man of medium height and athletic build who loved sports, rock music and literature. He was two years old when his family moved to a new home in the suburb of the Biltmore, an upscale neighborhood in West Havana, which was later on renamed *Siboney*. It was a nice wooded area of the city, not too far from the coast and cooled by a perennial ocean breeze.

By the end of 1960, the mass exodus that followed Castro's takeover turned Siboney into a ghost town. The neighborhood remained virtually abandoned for several years, and then became slowly re-populated with foreign embassies, diplomatic residences and technical advisors from the Soviet bloc. Some of the top higher-ups in Castro's government—the *Mayimbes*—also moved in with their families, along with a few hundred country girls brought in to study at a nearby boarding school. After forcing thousands of people to leave, Fidel became the supreme landlord of everything on the island, including hundreds of elegant homes and sumptuous mansions worth millions of dollars.

In 1969, Nick's family was one of the last original residents still living within two square miles south of Fifth Avenue near the old University of Villanova campus. Most of their former neighbors had either left the country, or were relocated to less affluent areas of the city. By then, the family had become a living relic of a past long gone.

In the years prior to Castro, Nick attended St. Thomas Military Academy—not quite a reform school, but still tough enough to instill discipline, moral values and respect in the young cadets. He excelled in fencing and judo and became a competitive swimmer at the Comodoro Yacht Club. He also loved spending hours reading in his home's library. With dozens of books of every possible genre waiting to be explored, Nick immersed himself in a world of knowledge and exciting adventures. Over time, he developed a passion for science books and aspired to become an engineer like his father.

His dreams, however, started to vanish the day Castro's bearded rebels stomped into the streets of Havana. All the private schools were shut down and replaced with a deeply politicized public school system. Within months, the regime implemented a Soviet-style indoctrination program to run parallel to the academic curriculums. Political studies on Marxism and Leninism became mandatory subjects for all students attending the elementary schools, high schools and universities.

One of the first arbitrary mandates issued by the new government was the removal from the classrooms of all history books printed before 1959. The new editions covered only the years of Castro's armed insurgency, along with a few highly censored stories about the Cuban-Spanish war. With the stroke of a pen, the regime managed to erase decades of historical events from the country's past. Scores of significant personalities and political leaders who had forged the island's identity and its rich culture were also wiped-out from the country's recorded heritage.

The images of Jesus Christ, the Virgin Mary and the Catholic saints suffered a similar fate. They were replaced with portraits and busts of Marx, Engels, Stalin, Lenin and Mao Zedong, foreign philosophers and dictators of whom most Cubans have never heard before. Everyone on the island had no choice but to keep their own beliefs to themselves and pay public respect to the new secular Gods. Those who dared not to comply with the new rules of idolatry became the victims of verbal attacks and physical beatings by the mobs, or ended-up in prison without a trial.

Like most Cubans, Nick had to fake tolerance for the new laws of the land. Survival in such a toxic environment would depend on staying ahead of the game until he could find an exit. The expectation to leave, however, disappeared the day he turned fifteen years old and became of military age. His family had waited much too long for Castro's regime to either implode, or get overthrown. They found themselves stuck on the prison island with no way out.

In spite of the mounting pressures at school, Nick managed to stay away from politics. He never said yes or no to the Marxist recruiters who approached him, thus avoiding being dragged into their scheme through a persistent dithering. They eventually gave up on him.

Nevertheless, politics had become the core of the Marxist society. Those who strayed from the path set by the Communist party were marked as anti-social elements and promised an even bleaker future in the new society.

The insanity that had taken over his country puzzled Nick from day one. Why have so many people surrendered their values and freedoms and choose to worship a despot who kept them under the boot?—he kept wondering.

Was it because Castro possessed extraordinary powers of persuasion and a great charisma? Plausible, but that could only be part of the answer. By repeating over and over his well-rehearsed rhetoric, Fidel made the people believe that all sacrifices made for the benefit of the future generations was a noble and worthy cause. What Castro actually meant was that the present in Cuba was doomed—although not for him, his family and his closest collaborators.

"We must make great sacrifices for the sake of our children, and the children of our children," Castro would say over and over again.

An entire decade went by before an incident in Europe offered Nick a plausible explanation for the incredible social paradox that had overtaken the island.

In August of 1973, several employees of the Kreditbanken in Sweden were taken hostage by a group of armed thieves and held inside the bank's vault. After the six-day standoff, some of the victims became emotionally attached to their captors, and even went on to justify their violent behavior. Swedish renowned psychiatrist Nils Bejerot first named the condition the Norrmalstrong Syndrome, later known as the Stockholm syndrome.

The Kreditbank incident convinced Nick that thousands of Cubans could be indeed suffering from a chronic condition similar to the Stockholm syndrome, a bizarre social anomaly that have kept those compatriots in a deplorable state of blind submission for so many years.

The truth behind the hyped social equality the revolution had supposedly brought to the people lay hidden in plain sight. While the average Cuban struggled daily to fetch the meager food rations allocated by the regime, the elite class in power lived in overabundance and luxury. The *Mayimbes* traveled the world with all their expenses paid, owned vacation homes and drove new automobiles. Their families were issued multiple rationing cards and kept their kitchen pantries well stocked with every conceivable food staple. Their children wore American-made polyester shirts, Levi's jeans and Florsheim shoes and were chauffeured to school daily by armed bodyguards in new Alfa Romeo sedans.

In the mid-sixties, the young man had a firsthand encounter with the lavish lifestyle of the new elite class that ruled the island. The incident took place during a chance visit to the residence of Jesus Montané, the man in charge of the ministry of communications and one of Castro's commanders in the days of the armed insurrection against Batista. Nick had met Montané's son Sergio through a high school friend and was invited to spend an afternoon at his home in the upscale neighborhood of Miramar.

Perhaps trying to impress his guests, Sergio asked the boys to follow him to the kitchen where he opened a large chest freezer. As the cold vapor dissipated, Nick noticed the chest was packed to the rim with deer venison.

"My Dad just got back from hunting," Sergio told his friends with a smile.

Sergio's father was one of the few men allowed to own guns and hunt deer and other game on the island. Ironically, the freezer at the Montané's residence held more meat than an entire Cuban family was allowed to buy in a year or two.

A pantry door left ajar revealed cans of Hershey's dark cocoa, Tang powder juice, and corn flakes cereal—American-made products that had long disappeared from the Cuban stores. Nick was stunned by the finding but kept his revulsion to himself.

The visit to Sergio's home had just proven that the communist leaders in Cuba not only enjoyed undue privileges, but were some of the biggest hypocrites on the face of the earth.

It did not take long for Nick to put the pieces of the puzzle together. Montané's ministry censored every single letter and parcel post coming into the island. For years, most of the humanitarian shipments sent by Cubans living overseas to their relatives never reached its intended recipients. Instead, the packages were systematically diverted to the members of the elite class in power. Some of the beneficiaries of the looted parcels included the minister himself and the members of his immediate family.

As tough as it was, Nick had managed to keep his emotions under control and his mouth shut for a long time—that until one ill-fated afternoon at school. On that day, his good luck took a turn for the worse.

The incident took place during a political class called student forums. During the make-believe debates the students were not allowed to express their own opinions, or challenge the views of the political indoctrinator. The topics of the debates were usually chosen from the anonymous editorials published in the local newspaper Granma, which were presumably written by Fidel Castro himself. Such anonymity had a well though-out purpose, though. It shielded Fidel from being held accountable if he were to convey an opinion that could later prove to be either inaccurate, or outright wrong.

The subject of that day's debate was the relationship between Ché Guevara, an Argentinean-born guerrilla, and Regis Debray, a Left-wing French journalist who had established close ties with the Cuban regime since the early days of the revolution.

In the mid-sixties, Ché's mind was set on replicating Castro's revolution in other countries throughout the world. He had been to Africa in 1965 to join a Marxist-leaning revolt in the Republic of Congo. However, things didn't go well for Ché in Congo and was soon forced to retreat and return to Cuba in total defeat.

In 1968, Ché and a handful of his closest followers left the Caribbean island for yet another wild adventure, this time to wage a guerrilla war against the government of Rene Barrientos in the jungles of Bolivia.

Not long after Ché established camp deep inside the Bolivian mountains, Regis Debray followed in his tracks. The French journalist wanted to imitate the deeds of Herbert Matthews, a reporter from the New York Times who interviewed Fidel Castro in the Sierra Maestra mountains ten years earlier.

Debray's ultimate goal was to publish a series of pictorial articles in Paris and other European cities depicting the guerrilla as a quintessential Robin Hood fighting to liberate the peasants of Bolivia. His effort should help legitimize Ché's armed insurrection and gain him widespread international support.

But most significantly, it should open the funding spigots at the *6th Arrondissement*, a bohemian enclave in Paris where some of the wealthiest socialists of the world lived.

Nonetheless, fate had a different plan for Debray and Ché Guevara and the men under his command. In April of 1967, members of the Bolivian Special Forces arrested the Frenchman in the mountains outside La Paz as he tried to leave the country. In November of that same year, Regis Debray was convicted by a Bolivian military court of being a member of Ché's guerrilla force. Debray and his travelling companion, a man called Ciro Bustos, were sentenced to thirty years in a Bolivian prison.

A few months after Debray's arrest, Ché Guevara was captured by a detachment of Bolivian Army Rangers and executed without trial in the small town of La Higuera. In an irony of destiny, Ché's life ended the same way as hundreds of Cubans whose death sentence he signed personally during his tenure as head of the Cuban prison of La Cabaña.

Nick heard a news report about Debray's capture on the Voice of the Americas, a radio station sponsored by the U.S. Information Services. The station broadcasted its regular programming into Cuba on the 1,100-megahertz AM frequency, and on several shortwave radio frequencies.

In the early sixties, the Soviets switched on a powerful radio signal jammer at one of their Signals Intelligence facilities in Cuba. The purpose of the jammer was to interfere with the VOA transmissions by placing a loud humming sound on the same frequency. The ensuing noise, however, was hardly a nuisance and didn't discourage thousands of Cubans from listening to the freedom broadcasts in the privacy of their homes. It was the only voice of hope heard in Cuba, and a virtual window to the free world. Among many other important world events, thousands of Cubans on the island had the opportunity to listen live to the first

U.S. astronauts landing on the moon on the VOA radio.

One evening, the VOA commentator announced that Ché Guevara had been captured thanks to Regis Debray handing the coordinates of the guerrilla command post over to the Bolivian Intelligence Services.

Without giving it a second thought, Nick stood up to speak in front of the class.

"We have to consider the possibility that, under duress and physical torture, Debray could have revealed Ché's whereabouts to the Bolivian army."

It took Nick a second to realize he had said the wrong thing. A long and eerie silence followed. When he looked up at the political lecturer, the woman's face had turned purple with ire.

The woman started lashing out at the young man with an ear-piercing rebuke, accusing him of listening to the subversive programs of the Voice of the Americas radio. The majority, if not all the communist indoctrinators who taught in Cuban schools were either agents of the secret police, or worked as their informants. The DSE had likely asked them to listen to the VOA programming on a regular basis so they would know exactly what was being broadcasted into the island. The school indoctrinator had obviously heard the same VOA report about Debray having spilled the beans on Ché.

"Debray is a proven socialist who would have never betrayed Ché under any circumstances. A true revolutionary never breaks down even under the greatest duress. You are a shameless bourgeois and a reactionary. I'll see that you don't set one foot in this school again. You may leave the class now and wait for me at the principal's office," the woman told him.

Nick got expelled from school and a letter was placed in his file as a permanent record of his transgression. In the principal's eyes, the young man had committed the unforgivable crime of displaying a politically disruptive attitude in front of his classmates. He had become a saboteur.

His expulsion from school was just the beginning of his troubles. Within a week, a young soldier in uniform showed up at his doorstep to hand-deliver the dreaded telegram from the Ministry of the Army. The regime had decided to draft him into the SMO, the conscript military service.

"Never lose hope," his father told him. "One day you will look back and see the time spent in the army as an insignificant episode in your life."

Chapter 3

At the age of twelve or thirteen, Nick was already sketching out rafts he hoped to build someday to escape from the island. He drew the designs furtively while at school, at home and practically anywhere he found a pencil and paper. Sometimes, he would add a spark of black humor by drawing shark fins on the water or large ships with the Soviet sickle-and-hammer flag sailing on the horizon. Building a seaworthy raft became his secret obsession.

That night in bed, he read the telegram from the Ministry of the Army for the hundredth time. With less than two weeks to report for boot camp, he decided it was time to sail away.

The makeshift raft he had in mind called for a few components that would be relatively easy to procure, and to hide from sight. He needed two large tire inner tubes, half-dozen burlap sacks, the hammered-out sides of an old wood ladder, a paddle and about fifty feet of half-inch braided rope.

In principle, building the raft would not be too difficult. After inflating the inner tubes, he would wrap them with the burlap sacks to protect the rubber from the sun and keep them from becoming punctured by an exposed reef, or by floating debris. He would fasten the inner tubes to the ladder sides with the braided rope, then weave two nets over the inner tube openings—one to use as a seat, the other to hold a water jug and a few cans of food.

Emulating the exploits of Arsene Lupin, a fictional French thief and one of his childhood heroes, Nick broke into a bus repair shop and made out with two new, deflated inner tubes. Over the years, his father had saved many burlap sacks that once held chicken feed and had been stacked in the backyard shed, along with several rolls of braided rope. His old tire pump should do the trick to inflate the inner tubes, and a brass-encased compass he had removed from his father's theodolite would help him navigate his way north.

The voyage would require some vigorous paddling for at least two to three miles offshore. With a little bit of a tailwind, and good luck, he could reach a northeastward ocean current known as the Gulf Stream in a matter of hours. If the books he had read on the subject were true, the Gulf Stream should carry him to the eastern Florida seaboard in three to four days. One of the many ships that sailed the Florida Straits, or a U.S. Coast Guard cutter, could rescue him.

On the flip side of the coin, he could face some serious dangers while underway. He could be spotted by a Cuban torpedo boat, or by one of the many cargo ships from communist bloc countries that sailed in and out of Cuba regularly. There was also a chance of getting lost in the middle of the ocean, running out of food and water, or drowning.

With the materials for the raft secured and hidden in the backyard shed, his next challenge was to find a safe staging place to put everything together and launch. He lived less than half a mile from the ocean and knew the area like the palm of his hands. However, Havana's entire coastline was patrolled day and night by machine-gun toting soldiers and police dogs. There were hardly any places to hide from sight and stage his escape.

The men and women who lived in that neighborhood posed a serious threat. Most were hard-core fanatics who now occupied the homes of Cubans forced into exile by Castro's regime. Any of those loyalists could call the police if they suspected that he was trying to flee from the island. Over time, thousands of radicalized fanatics in Cuba had done unspeakable harm to their fellow countrymen just to gain favor with the regime, or to escalate to higher positions of power.

He rode his bike up and down the littoral for a week looking for a place to launch his raft. In the end, he decided on a small rocky inlet next to a private home on the water. A thick sea grape bush near the inlet would help him stay out of sight, assemble the raft and wait for the right moment to launch.

The teenager started counting the days and hours until the next moonless night. He tuned in daily to WQAM, a radio station from Miami on the 560 AM radio dial. WQAM's signal came inside Cuba with great clarity and offered the weather report for South Florida and the Keys on the hour. Although the forecast's coverage area was more than one hundred miles away, the WQAM reports were a fairly good indicator of the general weather conditions in the Florida straits. Nick didn't believe anything the Cuban radio said, and had learned to distrust the local weather reports and storm advisories. They were wrong ninety percent of the time.

On the date set for the launch, WQAM predicted relatively calm seas with some chances of thunderstorms, along with a light wind blowing from the northeast. The wind direction was far from ideal, but Nick could not afford to postpone his escape until the next moonless night. If he got caught trying to flee the country after joining the military, he would be sent to a court martial for desertion.

One piece at a time, Nick transported the raft parts on his bike to the staging spot under the sea grape bush. Inflating the large inner tubes using the old hand pump was noisy and took him longer than he had anticipated. Weaving the nets was also a slow and painstaking task. Twice, he was forced to stop his work and lay down flat on his stomach—holding his breath while the two-man border patrol and their dog walked by just a few yards from his hideout.

A gust of cold wind from the north warned him that the weather was turning. Going out to sea under those conditions was not a sound decision, but he would launch regardless. He checked the raft for the last time and secured his provisions and water jug into the net he had woven on the second inner tube. By then, his heart was racing in his chest at a hundred miles per hour.

A light drizzle started to fall around midnight, coinciding with the arrival of the border patrolmen for the third time that evening. Again, it took about ten minutes for the soldiers and their leashed dog to walk by and then disappear once again around a bend on the shore.

It was time to go. Nick pulled the heavy raft from the hideout, dragged it into the water and climbed on board. He could not remember ever feeling so rushed, or being so terrified in his life.

He had been paddling for half an hour on a raft that refused to hold a heading when he ran into the first breaking wave. The surf pushed him back a good ten yards before a second wave crested unexpectedly in front of him. That one was huge, forceful and unforgiving. Nick let go of the safety rope seconds before the raft flipped over and dropped him into the dark waters.

The young man was an accomplished swimmer, but the strong riptide he encountered that night almost made him drown. When he surfaced, his raft was nowhere to be seen. He started swimming back toward the city lights. A dog's bark in the distance announced that the border patrol was on the rebound. Soon enough, he realized he had drifted with the current and would be coming ashore a few blocks west of his launch point.

As he got close to the rocky shore, a receding wave shoved him against a shallow reef. The razor-like coral ripped through his shirt, lacerating the flesh of his right thigh. He got out of the water and ran toward the only hiding place in sight—a concrete slab broken in two that lay tilted against the seawall. He squeezed his body under the concrete structure trying to keep a rusty piece of rebar from slashing his back open.

The skies opened up and the drizzle turned into a heavy downpour. Lightning struck nearby, followed by a deafening thunder. A second lightning bolt lit the beach in front of him, revealing the silhouettes of two rifle-toting soldiers struggling to keep their poncho hoods from getting blown by the wind. The leashed German shepherd kept on barking and pulling his handler towards his hideout. The dog had probably seen him, or picked-up his scent. Luckily, the guards did not pay attention to the canine and kept on walking.

The lighting show offered Nick occasional glimpses of his raft being tossed back and forth on the horizon. While he had failed in his escape attempt, he was lucky to have walked away with his life and evade capture. Had the soldiers found him that night, they would have beaten him up and sent him straight to a labor camp. His parents would not have known of his fate until weeks, or even months later.

"How did you manage to get so messed up?" The pretty nurse at the community clinic asked Nick. She had been inspecting his wounds with visible concern.

"It was a stupid fall. I slipped and fell from the seawall while fishing in the rain, and landed smack on the dog-tooth rocks below." After recovering his bike, Nick rode back to his house around four o'clock that night. He dressed the larger wounds with gauze and then decided to pay a visit to the clinic the following morning. Some of the cuts had already started to show signs of early infection.

"I'm afraid those two large cuts on your leg will need stitches. I will clean and disinfect the other abrasions, but the doctor will have to take care of the rest. By the way, my name is Carmen."

"I'm Nick. I like the name Carmen. It goes perfectly with a pretty woman like you."

"Flattery will get you nowhere," she snickered.

"Carmen, there is this great movie I have wanted to see for a long time, but I hate going to the theater alone. I bet you have not seen it either."

"You are too fast for me. I hardly know you."

"You can't blame me for trying. Does that mean yes?"

"Maybe you can call me sometime and we can talk about this on the phone. The doctor will see you now."

Carmen stood pensive for a few seconds. She then wrote down her phone number on a piece of paper, handed it to Nick and left the room with a smile.

The following weekend, Nick took Carmen to watch a rerun of *That Man from Rio* with Jean-Paul Belmondo. The French movie had been a ticket box success when it first showed in Havana and was playing again at a second-tier cinema in the old part of the city. After the movie, the couple went for a walk on the nearly deserted Central Park Boulevard.

"A few years ago, my family and I applied to leave Cuba via Spain. I have an aunt in the United States who got us the visas to enter in Spain and the money for the plane tickets. On the same day we applied for the permit to leave the country, my father got fired from his job and sent to a sugar cane plantation in Camaguey."

"How long has he been there?" Nick asked.

"My dad has already served most of the three-years of forced labor mandated by the regime. We hope to get the permit to leave the country in a matter of months, if not weeks. You and I won't see each other ever again." Carmen said somberly.

"Carmen, I must confess that I lied to you at the community clinic. My injuries were not caused from falling off a seawall as I claimed happened, but from landing on a shallow reef while trying to escape by raft the night before. I nearly drowned in the attempt. You and I happen to think the same way."

"You are crazy. I could read in your eyes that your story was not true. You looked like you were in deep shock."

"That attempt was my last chance to escape, at least for now. I have to report for the compulsory military service in five days. But that does not mean I won't try again."

"Don't be foolish. Too many people have died attempting to leave that way. I'll promise to write to you lots of letters, and we can see each other on your free days before I leave," Carmen whispered.

After Nick joined the military, it was Carmen's long letters what kept his spirits up and his motivation alive. He would lie down in his bunk and read them over and over again.

The joy of Carmen's wonderful friendship would be short-lived. Without warning, the Cuban immigration police showed-up one morning at her home in Havana. The family hardly had enough time to pack one small suitcase each and rush to the airport to make their flight.

Nick, who was deployed at a base in Pinar del Rio one hundred and fifty miles away, never had a chance to say good-bye. He didn't find out about Carmen's departure for Spain until her farewell letter was delivered to him two weeks later.

Adiós Carmen. C'est la vie.

Chapter 4

In the fall of 1968 Nick's sister Militza was expelled from school when she made the mistake of challenging a political indoctrinator. The teacher had been spewing anti-American rhetoric during class when she could not take his lies any longer and spoke her peace. She was dragged to the principal's office and told to never return to that school again.

The incident was almost identical to what happened to Nick two years earlier, but the reaction from her school principal was harsher that time around. The principal, a radical communist and saboteur from the days of Castro's urban warfare, accused Militza of being a mercenary in the service of the United States. He told her that her counter-revolutionary attitude in class would be reported to the secret police.

"Don't be surprised if they send you to the UMAP. That's the only suitable place for antisocial elements like you," the principal told her.

The mention of the word UMAP brought a chill to the young woman's spine. In the mid sixties, the regime had built an undisclosed number of concentration camps throughout the island. Those internment camps were known as the UMAP, the acronym for military units for the aid of production.

Over time, thousands of young men and women who dared to display pro-American tendencies were locked up in the camps without due legal process. Also sent into forced internment were scores of Christians, Jehovah's Witnesses, Jews, gays, lesbians and prostitutes.

The camps filled-up fast. Castro's police started conducting flash raids in Havana and other cities, mostly at night. They would load up the youngsters on army trucks and cattle trains and then shipped them straight to the UMAP camps in Camaguey and other remote areas of the country. In most cases, their families were not notified of their children's fate until many weeks later. Between 1965 and 1968, thousands of young Cubans were kept confined behind barbed wire fences under the worst living conditions imaginable.

The UMAP prisoners were housed in barracks with dirt floors, slept in jute hammocks, and had no clean water or sanitary services. They were fed meager food rations of Russian canned meat, sardines and pasta. Their bodies were covered with infected scabs and insect bites, and the vast majority of them suffered from chronic dysentery and other serious ailments. Many young prisoners committed suicide, while others died as a result of torture and diseases.

The young men and women whom Castro had branded as social misfits and degenerates were forced to work day in and out, under the watch of armed guards, planting and harvesting sugar cane, picking *boniato* roots, and cutting fields of thorny marabou overgrowth with dull machetes. Their only crime had been to be freethinkers in the Cuban totalitarian society.

With the horrors of the UMAP lurking in her mind, Militza returned home with her eyes drenched in tears.

Fearing the school principal would make good on his threats, her father—Victor Daniels Nickolich—reached out to an old friend for help. His last hope was William Powe, a former business partner from the Caterpillar dealership in Havana. Powe had left Cuba in 1960 and resettled with his family in his hometown of Hattiesburg, Mississippi. He was also Militza's godfather.

Victor Daniels plead didn't go unanswered. Powe promised him to get Militza a tourist visa into Mexico, buy her an airplane ticket and see that she would be taken care of in that country until she could enter the United States.

Zulema Nasser was a well-connected woman of Lebanese heritage whom Victor Daniels and Ramona Nickolich had met at a reception at the Embassy of Lebanon. Every year, on November 22nd, the family had been invited to the dinner in celebration of Lebanon's day of independence. The embassy was located right across the street from the Nickolich family home in Siboney.

The family had attended the dinner every year, but not in 1963. On that ill-fated afternoon, the ambassador called Victor Daniels to advise him that the dinner had been cancelled. The airwaves had just brought the news that U.S. President John Fitzgerald Kennedy had been assassinated in the streets of Dallas.

"I just got a call from Zulema," Militza told her father a few days later. "She said that Korda is coming to our house tomorrow to take some family pictures."

When Zulema heard of Militza's impending departure for the United States, the woman arranged for the well-known photographer to take their family pictures. She thought it would be a great memory for both Militza and her parents to have.

Ironically, Alberto Korda was Fidel Castro's personal photographer, and the man who took the infamous picture of Ché Guevara that would gain him worldwide notoriety. It was the image of Ché's face that so many youngsters would get to wear on their tee shirts for decades to come. Unfortunately, most of those people were oblivious that Ché was not just an adventurer, but a merciless killer who sent hundreds of Cubans to the firing squad without a trial.

After some string pulling and paying off an immigration official, Militza was allowed to leave for Mexico City. For her parents, the farewell was an unspeakable heartbreak. The moment the airplane's wheels lifted off the ground, Nick felt as if his sister was already a thousand light-years away. She had just turned nineteen years old.

Not long after his sister left Cuba, Nick thought it was time for him to plan his early discharge from the military. He had served ten months as an army medic in a remote field hospital in Pinar del Rio and had enough of the political brainwashing, the lousy food and the harsh living conditions. It was time for him to test his luck again.

One night while on sentry duty, Nick yelled out to another guard that a horde of Solarian robots was descending from the starry skies onto the base. He took off the safety on his AK-47 rifle and started firing the weapon in full automatic bursts above the officer's quarters. When he ran out of bullets, he dropped his gun on the ground and climbed up a large tree. Two MPs eventually talked him down, restrained him with a rope and locked him up in a makeshift jail.

The next morning, the base commander found the science fiction book that Nick had left intentionally on top of his pillow as part of his plot. It was a worn-out paperback copy of Isaac Asimov's *The Naked Sun*.

The science-fiction novel was about a planet antagonistic to earth where robots had taken over and outnumbered the native Solarians ten thousand to one.

"This explains the strange names that Nick had been calling his superiors by in the past weeks. Make sure the doctors know he was reading this book," the base commander instructed his military police escort.

Nick spent two days at the naval hospital in eastern Havana, after which he was sent home to recover under his parent's care. After several visits to the hospital, a team of doctors diagnosed him with a severe nervous breakdown. His discharge papers arrived two months later.

When Nick tried to enroll back in school, he got turned down everywhere he applied. The reason was not his early release from the military as he had thought, but the smearing paper that the school principal had placed in his student file a year earlier. The dark specter of Regis Debray and Ché Guevara kept haunting him long after their demise in the mountains of Bolivia.

In the summer of 1969, Nick landed a job as an English translator at the University of Havana. His passion for reading had improved the fundamental English he had learned at St. Thomas. By the time he was sixteen years old, he had read most of the books stacked in his home library—from Graham Greene, to Edgar Allan Poe, Mark Twain, Fyodor Dostoyevsky and Walt Whitman, all in English. He passed the admission test with flying colors.

That time around, he made sure not to mention his school problems or his premature discharge from the army on the job application. The university would have never employed him had they known about his turbulent past. Against the dictates of his heart, the young rebel would go on living his life in the shadow of deceit.

Cuba was in dire need of a radical change to restore the freedoms and human rights lost to the Marxists in power. Like many men and women on the island, Nick often dreamed of an internal rebellion that would overthrow the Castros from power. Unfortunately, there was not one chance in a million for such a dream to come true—at least not while the regime still counted with thousands of opportunists and cutthroats as their loyal supporters.

Armed to the teeth with Russian and Chinese weapons, the Cuban army had become exceptionally powerful, highly politicized, but fearful of the secret police. Fear in itself became deeply embedded in every aspect of life in Cuba. Everyone on the island was afraid to say, or do anything that could be viewed as antagonistic to Fidel, or to the Marxist doctrine. The mere insinuation of dissatisfaction with the regime, spoken in the wrong place, would be equivalent to committing suicide.

Over the years, the State Security apparatus had successfully recruited thousands of informants at workplaces, schools, sports centers, farms, and virtually everywhere on the island. While some people spied on their peers voluntarily, most informants had been blackmailed into that role after being caught committing petty crimes such as buying supplementary food in the black market.

The DSE tactics were shrewd indeed. Whenever a targeted victim refused to collaborate, he or she would be threatened to be sent to prison without a trial. It wasn't long before the country got filled with snitches who wrote regular reports on their friends and fellow citizens.

Consequently, everyone in Cuba became weary to speak candidly to one another and doubted the integrity of even their closest friends and family members. There was no way of telling who was sincere, or who was working covertly for the DSE. Many informants would even pretend to be anti-Communist just to put to the test the other person's loyalty to the regime. Sadly enough, Cuba had turned into a police state in every sense of the word.

To expect a mutiny to sprout within the government itself was another pipe dream. From the start, Castro had effectively silenced every single manifestation of dissent against his power, thus sending a strong message to the rest of his followers—the Marxist leader would not tolerate any challenges to his authoritarian powers. For Nick, and many others like him, the only hope left was to find a way to flee from the prison island and start a new life elsewhere.

THE LYNX

Chapter 5

Less than an hour's drive from Havana lay the windswept basin of Lake Ariguanabo, a broad expanse of shallow wetlands that once covered more than ten square miles south of the town of Bauta.

In 1970, Nick had become a frequent visitor to the lake together with Michael Quinn, the first secretary of the British Embassy and his next-door neighbor. A career diplomat with the British Foreign Service, Michael was an amateur photographer and ornithologist. Michael often told Nick of his dream of making a pictorial essay of the North American waterfowl that wintered in the marshes of western Cuba. The Brit hoped that his article would be published someday in the glossy pages of the National Geographic magazine.

However, Nick suspected there was more about Michael's interest in photography than met the eye. As every other diplomat from the U.K. deployed overseas, his intriguing neighbor probably was a covert agent for MI6—the British Military Intelligence Services.

Nick met Michael and Annabel Quinn the day the British couple moved to the residence next door. He had been reading under the shade of a tree when he heard an animated conversation on the other side of the wall. He grabbed a ladder and climbed up to investigate.

Standing on the neighboring lawn was a tall man in his late twenties next a slender brunette. The young couple was looking up at a tree branch loaded with fruit that overlapped the property wall.

"Those are mangoes," Nick said. "You are welcome to have as many as you like."

That fortuitous encounter was the spark to a great friendship. From that day on, he would spend hours at the Quinn's playing backgammon, contract bridge, or just listening to the latest albums of the Beatles, the Rolling Stones and other British pop bands. Other than his own home, the Quinn's residence was the only place where he could breathe freely and disconnect from the austerity that reigned on the rest of the island.

That winter, Nick and Michael made several day trips to Lake Ariguanabo. The men spent hours walking on the lake's edge and scouting the marsh for ducks and birds that migrated every winter from North America. For many years in the pre-Castro era, those migrations had signaled the beginning of the waterfowl-hunting season on the island.

That old tradition, however, disappeared in 1959 when the regime pulled the plug on the citizen's rights to own firearms. The new hunters were a select group of men in the dictator's innermost circle who had been given unlimited access to the hunting preserves set aside by the regime.

It was during one of those road trips, away from snooping ears and hidden microphones when Nick told Michael about his obsession to flee from Cuba. He had found someone willing to listen—someone he could trust.

"There ought to be a way out of here for you, Nick," Michael often told him. Never give up hope.

A few weeks later, Nick was introduced to Camille Bouchet at the Quinn's New Year Eve's reception. Camille was the attractive daughter of the French Ambassador to Havana.

That night, Nick and Camille spent most of the evening talking about music, art, and of Nick's dreams of escaping from Cuba. By the time the goblets filled with *Veuve Clicquot* were raised to celebrate the New Year, Camille and Nick had become great friends.

Camille didn't wait long to share Nick's thoughts with her father and asked him to help her friend get out of the island. One evening at the dinner table, Monsieur Bouchet whispered a secret in his daughter's ear.

"I just paid a courtesy visit to one of our cargo ships docked at the port of Havana," the ambassador told her. "The captain seems to be a kind and reasonable man. I will see him again tomorrow and ask him if he's willing to take Nick aboard his ship and bring him to France."

"How would you get him on the ship?" Camille asked her father with excitement.

"If the captain agrees with my idea, your brothers Jean-Claude and Pierre can escort him to the ship and get him on board by flashing their diplomatic passports. The ship's officers and sailors go in and out all the time to hang out in the local bars. Three young and well-dressed men should not arise suspicion, particularly since Nick doesn't look Cuban. It's a long shot, but one that might work"

"I'm so proud of you *Papa*. Thank you."

"We'll see. With some luck, your friend could be on his way to Marseilles in a few days."

Monsieur Bouchet brought his daughter the good news the following evening.

"The captain told me he will not object to hide Nick aboard the ship and take him to France as long as we can get him up there undetected. Understandably, he wants to avoid problems with the port authorities if someone were to suspect he had a stowaway on board. I will explain to Jean-Claude and Pierre exactly what they need to do."

Camille wanted to run and tell Nick the news right away, but her father asked her not to say a word about the plot—not yet.

On the day set for the caper, Jean-Claude and Pierre showed up at Nick's house late in the afternoon. They asked him to dress up. Camille wanted him to join her for a cocktail party at their house.

It was only after Jean-Claude drove past the street where the French ambassador lived that Nick realized they were going somewhere else.

"There has been a slight change of plans. We are going to pay a visit to a French cargo ship at the port of Havana," Pierre told him.

"I can't wait," he said.

The three men got their first glimpse of the French cargo steamer as the Renault sedan made it past the Castillo de la Fuerza. The ship was moored gently at a pier on the west side of the harbor and there seemed to be very little activity on board. Nick was curious about a series of lines, letters and numbers painted on the ship's hull just above the water line.

"What's the meaning of those markings?" he asked.

"They are called Plimsoll lines. When they are visible, it means the ship has been relieved of her cargo and is ready to accept a fresh consignment," Jean-Claude replied.

Nick caught on the double meaning and smiled. Jean-Claude left the car parked curbside on the boulevard and headed over to the pier followed by Nick and Pierre on his heels. As the men approached the ship's gangplank, a rifle-toting guard took a step forward to block their way.

"How can I help you?" the guard asked the men.

"We are from the French Embassy on a courtesy visit to the ship," Jean-Claude told the guard while flashing his diplomatic passport. Pierre did the same.

"I need to see your passport," the guard told Nick.

"I'm sorry, but I left mine at the house," he answered.

The guard moved out of the way to allow Jean-Claude to pass, then Nick and Pierre. As the men started up the gangplank, the soldier suddenly ordered them to stop.

"I must see all your passports. I have strict orders not to allow anyone on board without proper documentation."

Jean-Claude realized he had to move fast. He feared the guard might want to question them further and blow their friend's cover. If the police found out that a Cuban national was trying to board the ship under false pretenses, they would arrest him and charge him with attempting to leave the country illegally. That was considered a very serious crime in Cuba and one that would invariably send anyone to prison for a long time.

"No problem. We'll come back later on tonight," said Jean-Claude, turning around and motioning Nick and Pierre to follow him back to the car.

Back at the French ambassador's residence, Nick thanked Monsieur Bouchet for talking to the ship's captain on his behalf and praised Jean-Claude's and Pierre's for their bravery. The men agreed that it would be too risky to make another attempt to board that particular ship. Maybe there would be another opportunity in the future.

The young man never had a second chance to sail away from Cuba aboard a cargo ship. Ambassador Bouchet's tenure in Cuba ended that month and the family returned to their home in Paris. Standing alone on the windy terrace at the airport, he watched as Camille turned around at the top of the airplane stairs to blow him a farewell kiss.

Au revoir, Camille!

He wrote several letters to Camille, but got only one back. He suspected the secret police had been reading and destroying his correspondence all along.

Nick often reflected back on that fateful day, wondering how his life would have turned out had he managed to get past the overly zealous guard at the dock. It had been heartbreak to get so close to being free and then missing the mark. It was not his time yet, he conceded. Besides, nothing of real significance had ever come easy to him.

The events that would set the decisive course for his future would not occur until years later and under very different circumstances.

Chapter 6

Lake Ariguanabo, 1971

A late summer outing to the lake would turn into a foretelling chapter in the young man's life. Nick had been hiking with Michael along the lake's northern banks when he spotted a flock of Mallards swimming behind a thick Sawgrass bush. He halted and gave his friend a subtle tap on the shoulder.

"Michael, get your camera ready," he whispered.

The Brit had started to mount his 35 mm Nikon on a monopod when they heard a rapid sequence of loud thuds above them. High over some scattered clouds were four deployed parachutes.

Startled by the explosive sound, the Mallard ducks took sudden flight skimming the shallow waters and disappeared from sight.

"Well, there go the bloody birds. Looks like those chutes are heading for Cayo la Rosa." Michael said. "Maybe we can get there on time to watch the parachutists land."

The men hurried back to Michael's Triumph convertible and sped south toward the small inland key. The multicolored round canopies in the skies ahead of them appeared to be traveling fast. Nick had seen parachutes above the lake before, but never that close. As the got near Cayo la Rosa, they noticed a yellow AN-2 biplane coming in for landing.

They made it to the small town just in time to watch the parachutists disappear behind a palm forest. Nick asked Michael to leave the car parked next to a baseball field and walk the few blocks that separated them from the airport. A Triumph TR6 with diplomatic license plates would have caused suspicion if noticed outside a government facility, particularly at a parachute training center. They decided that Nick should do all the talking.

A young man in olive drab pilot coveralls and flight boots greeted them at the airport gate.

"How can I help you, comrades?" the man asked.

"We were about a mile north from here when we saw parachutes heading this way. Can we watch up close?"

"Unfortunately, that was the last drop of the day," the man said. "We' are done jumping until seven tomorrow morning."

"I guess we are out of luck. Is this a military facility?"

"No. We have been open as a civilian parachute club for over a year."

"That's fantastic. Where can I sign up?"

"Joining the club is not easy. But if you really want to jump, it could be worth your while. You need to get approved by the club's director, pass a medical exam, and then go through an intensive jump school."

"If I join, how long before I'll get to jump out of an airplane?"

"The training can take anywhere from six to eight weeks."

The man pulled a paper from his pocket, scribbled something on it with a pencil and handed it over to Nick.

"Here is the club office address in El Vedado. You can tell the secretary there that you spoke to Collazo at Cayo la Rosa. I'm one of the jump instructors here."

On the drive back home, Nick could not think of anything else but the amazing parachutes he had seen in the sky above the lake. He had read books on airborne assaults during World War II, and watched scores of parachute drops in the movies. When he was barely nine years old, he almost broke his legs taking a leap of faith from his roof while holding onto the corners of a bed sheet. His longing to defy gravity was somehow difficult to explain.

Something else at Cayo la Rosa had caught his attention. The AN-2 he saw on final approach to the airfield had the door open, thus indicating it was the same plane used to drop the jumpers. Nick knew that the Russian AN-2s had an extended range and could fly all the way to the United States. If he got accepted into the club, he might find a way to take command of an AN-2 to escape from the island.

He knew better than to get his hopes up, though. Sport parachuting had to be a very selective activity reserved for militants in the Communist Party, or the Communist Youth. Because the sport involved the use of airplanes, the State Security would decide who could and could not participate. He just had to give it a shot and try to lie his way through the admission process. Maybe he could manage to sneak past the government filters undetected.

"You are serious about making a parachute jump?" Michael asked.

"I must admit that I'm inspired. But I'm not sure the government will allow me to join. Activities like this are typically set aside for people with a proven loyalty to the regime."

"You have nothing to lose by trying," Michael told him. "If you want to jump out of airplanes that bad, don't hesitate to do whatever it takes. Lie through your teeth if you have to. If you don't, then nothing will ever change in your life."

Nick thanked Michael for his words of encouragement. That day, he realized the time had come to rewrite his past and try to infiltrate the haphazard world of fanatics who have kept Castro in power. It would be better to live on the edge and become proactive than remain a spectator waiting for some miracle to happen.

By the time he got home, he had already decided to create a real opportunity for himself, an opportunity that could change his life forever. He would start out by becoming a skydiver.

Chapter 7

From the end spring new beginnings.
— *Gaius Plinius Secundus*

Victor Daniels Nickolich visited the island of Cuba for the first time in 1925. He sailed from Tampa to Havana aboard a former cargo steamer that had been converted into a passenger ferry boat. In a casual conversation with the skipper, he learned there were nearly an equal number of vacationers and immigrants registered on the ship's manifest. People were flocking to the island by the hundreds from every corner of the world.

It didn't take long for the engineer to understand why Cuba appealed to so many. Soon enough, he started appreciating the island's temperate climate, the ever-changing landscapes, the friendly people and the rambling cosmopolitan culture. Havana was bustling with streetcars, automobiles, restaurants, theaters, broad boulevards and fancy hotels. There were white sandy beaches, beautiful mountains and pristine valleys, along with a vast electric grid that brought power to the most remote areas of the country. It was paradise found.

Six years later, Victor Daniels and his brother Luca decided to take permanent residence on the island. The United States was going through the greatest economic depression in its history and Cuba's growing economy offered plenty of jobs and business opportunities. Investors, entrepreneurs, professionals, and regular folks from all over had set their sights on the Caribbean heaven to start their lives anew.

Victor Daniels found his niche in Cuba designing irrigation systems for the sugar cane plantations spawning rapidly throughout the tropical landscape. Luca, on the other hand, got a part-time job as a maître d' at the *Hotel Inglaterra* and enrolled at the University of Havana to finish medical school. Then tragedy struck. Less than a year after the brothers arrived in Cuba, Luca passed away unexpectedly from rheumatic fever. The sudden loss of his brother was a heartbreak from which Victor Daniels never fully recovered.

In 1943, Victor Daniels returned briefly to Tampa. He took flying lessons at a local airfield, got his pilot's license and bought a second-hand, two-seat Stinson airplane with cloth-covered wings.

He flew the airplane to the Florida Keys, and then hopped over the Florida Straits to Havana. In Cuba, he would fly the Stinson regularly in and out small dirt roads and open fields to reach the most remote plantations on the island. The plane soon became an efficient way to bring his business to the farmers and settlers, giving him a solid edge over the competition.

While attending a dance gala in Havana, Victor Daniels fell in love with a beautiful green-eyed woman named Ramona. They married a year later and had two children, Militza and Nick. In 1953, the family moved into a new home in a suburban neighborhood of Havana. By that time, Victor Daniels had bought a second airplane and invested most of his savings in a small rice farm with a grass airstrip near the town of San Cristobal. The farm was known as *Finca Los Pinos*.

When General Fulgencio Batista fled Cuba on New Year's Eve of 1959, Victor Daniels was one of many Americans on the island who hoped that Fidel Castro would become a positive game changer. At that moment in history, Fidel had both the potential and the people's support to deliver the democracy, harmony and prosperity he promised while fighting in the mountains. Still, many skeptics disagreed. They argued that those ideas could not be further detached from the leader's mind.

Castro's true colors didn't take long to surface. During a televised speech on December of 1961, Castro admitted for the first time to what many people had feared all along. In spite of his previous denials to that effect, he told the world that he was a Marxist-Leninist, and that he would stay as such until the end of his days. The veil of deceit had been lifted.

Now generously funded and supported by the Soviet Union, the dictator began his unstoppable drive to steer Cuba on the path to radicalization.

In 1960, thousands of Fidel's supporters were already thriving from the ensuing redistribution of wealth. Many of them had been rewarded for their loyalty with the keys to the homes and automobiles left behind by people gone into exile, along with their furnishings, clothes, silverware and works of art.

But others had backed Castro for a different reason. They were the honest blue-collar folks and peasants who loved their country and hoped it would flourish under the revolution. Unfortunately, those men and women would be duped into believing that communism was the only way to bring economic prosperity and social equality on the island. It wasn't long before their aspirations would collapse like a house of cards.

Like Adlai Stevenson, a former U.S. ambassador to the United

Nations once said, "Communism is the corruption of a dream of justice."

Ruling by decree, Castro nationalized every single foreign and domestic business concern in Cuba. Thousands of acres of productive land, industries, real estate, and small family-owned stores were confiscated from their owners without compensation. Newspapers, radio and TV stations were forced to close their doors, giving the regime absolute control over the broadcasted and printed media. Medical, dental and pharmaceutical private practices suffered the same fate, along with schools, universities and recreational centers.

By 1962, everything on the island was run by Castro's government. The only credentials required to manage an industrial, agricultural, or public service concern was to be a member of the Communist Party. Without skilled management and worker incentives, most enterprises in Cuba ran aground or imploded.

By placing all the means of production, education, and health care under government control, the so-called exploitation of men by men became the slavery of the people by the Communist state. In the name of equality, every person in Cuba was brought down to an equal level of poverty. Everyone but the members of the elite class in power.

The massive exodus that followed took a significant toll on the nation's intellectual population. By 1963, Cuba had already lost a significant percentage of its elite citizens, including doctors, architects, engineers, accountants, managers, and other professionals, as well as prominent personalities in the fields of business, science and the arts.

Not immune to the revolution's rage, Victor Daniels saw the fruit of decades of hard work disappearing. The small rice farm of Los Pinos, his investments in the Charco Redondo mines, several earth-moving machinery he leased to farmers and builders, and his two small airplanes were gone overnight. At age sixty-five and having seen healthier days, the American businessman was forced to join the ranks of the dispossessed.

While most of his friends and associates counted their losses and promptly left Cuba, the engineer opted to hunker down with his family in his Havana home as his last place of refuge. He conceded that he was too old to start all over again elsewhere. From that day on, Victor Daniels and many others on the island would survive by feeding on the false hopes that Castro's days were numbered.

"Eisenhower will never allow Cuba to become a satellite of the Soviet Union," Victor Daniels declared. "Not at ninety miles from the United States."

The TV anchorman had just announced that Castro was about to give a speech, prompting the engineer to get up from his chair and turn off the set. He had enough of the lies and the repetitive charade. Ramona, who called Castro *the beast*, would put her hands over her ears and leave the family room whenever Fidel's face popped up on their television screen. The bearded ogre in olive drab fatigues had become her worst living nightmare.

The Cuban dictator would soon become very predictable. During his televised speeches from a TV studio, or from his high rostrum at the José Martí Square, Castro would start out talking in a patriarchal tone of voice. That subdued tone made his listeners believe the dictator might have some good news that time around, or even offer some respite to the worsening state of austerity. It was what the people wanted to hear badly, thus they paid close attention.

In the end, their expectations would once again prove to be in vain. The stern Marxist-Leninist way of life was the only future that Castro had planned for Cuba, something he had no intentions of changing.

Fidel enjoyed reading to the people highly inflated statistics about the state of the economy. That part of his tedious monologue would go on for hours at a time. About three-quarters of the way into his discourse, Castro's tone of voice would become gradually louder and more aggressive as he veered toward political issues. For the thousandth time, he would blame the United States, the economic embargo and the enemies of the revolution for all of Cuba's misfortunes.

Invariably, the Cuban dictator would ask the people to make more personal sacrifices to counteract the foreign aggressions against Cuba. Toward the end of his speeches, Castro could be seen shaking his index finger up in the air and screaming from the top of his lungs as if he were on mind-altering drugs.

A hyped fear of both external and internal enemies plotting attacks against the revolution, along with the U.S. economic embargo became the tyrant's perennial excuse for failing to deliver prosperity to the Cuban people. The embargo had become a convenient pretext for the suppression of individual freedoms, the rationing of consumer goods and the perpetual state of asceticism and government dependency imposed on the people.

Time in Cuba had come to a virtual standstill—at high noon and under a scorching tropical sun.

"Castro will do the unimaginable to keep the economic blockade in place," Victor Daniels prophesied. "He needs the United States to remain his mortal enemy forever."

Regardless of the daily propaganda spewed by Castro and by the state-controlled media, the Cuban people knew the U.S. embargo was just a cleverly manipulated illusion. The economic blockade hardly prevented the government from purchasing anything they wanted in just about every country other than the United States.

By the mid-sixties, the Cuban economy was totally dependent on subsidies from the Soviet Union, China, and Eastern Europe. The Soviets and the Chinese had given Castro's regime vast weapons arsenals, along with industrial and agricultural technologies. Some of that was handed out to Cuba as part of a murky aid program, while the rest was paid for with sugar, coffee, fish, meat, and other domestic products sold at very low fixed prices.

Several banks from Canada, Mexico, France, Spain, Argentina, Italy, the Netherlands, and Japan extended liberal lines of credit to the regime for the purchase of raw materials, food, buses, heavy machinery, textiles, fertilizers, industrial equipment and spare parts. Castro never fell short of means to buy what the people of Cuba needed. Instead, most of that money got wasted in spreading the Communist doctrine overseas and to arm and finance terrorist groups worldwide.

When Cuba became fiscally insolvent and unable to pay its mounting foreign debt, Castro suspended all payments and defaulted on billions of dollars in international loans. The systematic evasion of its financial obligations by the Banco Nacional turned Cuba into one of the riskiest economies in the world.

The lending banks would eventually be forced to write off billions of dollars in Cuban debt and new money would then be poured into the bad investments. That lucrative and vicious circle allowed Castro's regime to thrive for decades. Ironically, much of the money that supported Cuba's communist regime came indirectly from the pockets of unsuspecting taxpayers and bank depositors in many industrialized countries from all over the world.

Chapter 8

Attorney Luisa Esquiroz was a charming lady who lived with her two daughters, Luisa and Margarita in a two-story house across the street from Nick's home. The families became good friends and Nick's sister signed-up to take ballet lessons in the studio that Luisa ran from her home.

Nick's most vivid memory of Luisa's home was her menacing dog, a jet-black Doberman pinscher with a stub for a tail and clipped pointy ears. The dog had the nasty habit of startling those passing by the house by showing-up unexpectedly on the second floor balcony, barking furiously and foaming from the mouth. The balcony had no protective railing, giving the illusion that the beast could jump onto the lawn below at any moment.

When Nick was eight or nine years old, he and his friends often rode their bikes doing circles in front of Luisa's house to tease the dog and watch him go wild. Still, they all prayed in secret that the Doberman wouldn't go crazy enough and take the dreaded leap.

In the spring of 1960, Luisa asked Victor Daniels to allow a group of students from the University of Havana to meet secretly at his house. The men were members of the Catholic diocese of the university and had been openly critical of Castro's impending relations with the Soviet Union. Because the new laws in Cuba made it illegal for three or more people to meet without prior government authorization, the group began to gather secretly in the homes of their sympathizers. Their golden rule to evade detection was to never meet at the same house twice.

Victor Daniels agreed to host one meeting and a date was set for the conclave. Luisa advised the members of the group not to enter the house and to move on if they were to spot any suspicious vehicles parked on the street, or if the light outside the garage was out—the sign that the house had been compromised.

On the agreed upon date, five young men showed-up at their door in ten to fifteen minute intervals. The first to arrive was Alberto Muller, the charismatic leader of the Catholic student movement. The men met in Victor Daniels' study for nearly two hours, then left as stealthy as they arrived.

A few weeks later, the city of Havana witnessed one the first open demonstrations against Castro's move to turn Cuba into a Communist state. Led by Alberto Muller, nearly one hundred university students staged a march to protest the visit to Cuba of Anastas Mikoyan, the deputy foreign minister of the Soviet Union. The protesters wanted to remove a floral offering with the sickle and hammer that Mikoyan had laid at the foot of the monument to José Martí, the apostle for the Cuban independence.

The students viewed the reed with the Soviet flag as an insult to the memory of Martí, Cuba's national independence hero and a lover of freedom and justice. In turn, they brought with them a wreath with the Cuban flag. As they got closer to the monument, the men started chanting in unison "revolution yes, communism no."

That was too much for Castro's fanatics to take. With a brutality not seen in Cuba since the years under Batista, the regime's repressive forces clubbed the demonstrators with sticks and the butts of their rifles, arrested scores of them and destroyed cameras belonging to reporters who had flocked to the Central Park when tipped of the impending rally.

Castro's militia stomped on the floral piece with the Cuban flag and set it on fire. On the run, Alberto Muller and other demonstrators stormed the grounds of the Brazilian Embassy in Havana. The men were granted political asylum by the Brazilian ambassador and eventually given safe passage out of the country.

Months later, Muller decided to return secretly to Cuba to fight alongside the anti-Castro guerrillas in the Escambray Mountains, but was captured by Castro's forces only days before the Bay of Pigs invasion. A Cuban mock tribunal sentenced the young courageous patriot to twenty years in prison.

In 1962, Luisa Esquiroz realized that life in Cuba had become too dangerous for a free thinker like her. She stopped briefly by Nick's house one evening to say goodbye to the family. The boy never got to know what happened to her mad Doberman.

In the summer of 1962 Castro ordered his internal security forces to conduct a house-to-house search and confiscate every firearm owned by civilians. The measure followed another rhetorical speech in which the dictator, in his olive drab fatigues and carrying a loaded Russian pistol at the waist posed a cynical question to his audience.

"Weapons for what, and to fight against who?"

Victor Daniels kept at home a .32 Cal semi-automatic pistol and a Colt .38 revolver for personal protection. When he learned the government had begun the house searches, the engineer wrapped the guns in a cloth soaked with motor oil and buried them in his backyard. Castro's militia eventually showed up at his house and searched every inch of the place, but didn't find the guns.

That same summer, the family got a scary visit from the G2, the Cuban repressive police. A sly looking man in plain-clothes showed-up unexpectedly at their door flashing the dreaded ID from the secret police.

"I'm Captain Varona from the G2," he said. The man walked up the stairs uninvited and made himself at home at the dining table.

"I am puzzled, *amigo* Nickolich. Isn't it unusual for an American expatriate to still be living in Cuba? Have you made plans to leave for the United States?" Varona asked.

"We are happy here. This country has been my home for thirty-some years. Cuba is also the birthplace of my wife and my two children."

Victor Daniels was worried about the sudden visit from a secret police captain. He feared that Varona was trying to find an excuse to incriminate him and evict them from his home. Rumors had it that a few people in Castro's regime had set their sights on their house. After looking with visible curiosity in every single room of the house, Varona left.

The following week, the G2 thug was back at their doorstep. By this time, Nick's father feared that the reasons for the man's visits were more convoluted than he had originally suspected. One question posed by the Varona clued him in on why the secret police had become so interested in him.

"Comrade, I believe that you are a friend of the revolution. However, we have many enemies both outside and inside our country. Would you tell us if you knew of anyone who might be conspiring to overthrow our people's government?"

Nick looked at his father and noticed his face had turned a shade paler.

"I would, Comrade Varona. But I don't know of anyone engaged in that kind of activity."

Victor Daniels now feared that someone had tipped the G2 of the secret meeting that Alberto Muller and his collaborators have had in his home.

His fears were not unfounded. A day after Varona's second visit, two plainclothes men arrived in an unmarked 1959 Chevrolet sedan and asked Victor Daniels to accompany them.

"It's only for routine questioning," the men told him.

The agents drove the engineer to a place known as *Quinta y Catorce*, the dreaded G2 political detention center located on the corner of Fifth Avenue and Fourteenth Street in the neighborhood of Miramar. Rumor had it that most men and women brought there for questioning were never seen or heard of again.

Worried about her husband's fate, Ramona placed a phone call Osvaldo Barrios. Barrios was a good friend of the family and the brother-in-law of Faustino Perez, one of the commanders of the rebel army during the insurrection. Barrios promised Ramona to make Faustino aware of the situation right away. The commander might be able to intercede with Castro and secure Victor Daniels' release from police custody before it was too late.

At *Quinta y Catorce*, the engineer was ushered into a dimly lit office with peeled paint and traces of graffiti on the walls. Moments later, Captain Varona marched in flanked by two other agents dressed in civilian clothes. All three men had a dreadful appearance and carried pistols tucked into their belts.

"Let's cut the BS. We know that some counterrevolutionary elements met secretly at your house not too long ago. I want their names."

"No such thing ever happened. You have mistaken me for someone else."

"Do you know a man named Alberto Muller?"

"I've never heard that name before. I want you to know that I have helped the revolution in the past."

That night, the engineer told the G2 men a story from the time he supervised a mining operation in the town of Charco Redondo in Oriente. The manganese and copper ore mines were located on the foothills of the Sierra Maestra and not far from Castro's base of operations during the guerilla war.

"Back in those troubled days, I risked my life by facilitating access to food, medicines and other supplies to the rebels that came down to the mining town almost every night. Because we kept a large amount of dynamite at the mine's premises, the facilities were guarded twenty-four seven by a small detachment of Batista's soldiers."

"Colonel Alberto del Rio Chaviano, the army commander in the province of Oriente, had placed the detachment under my orders. Acting against Chaviano's interests, I gave instructions to the soldiers to stay on lockdown at the garrison every night from dusk until dawn. I did it to allow the rebels an unchallenged passage into town at night to visit their families and gather food, medicines and other supplies."

Victor Daniels didn't tell Varona that the reason for his action was not to side with the rebels, but rather to prevent an unnecessary bloodshed that an encounter between the rebel forces and the soldiers would have caused.

"Had the military commander in Oriente found that I was helping the rebels," Victor Daniels said. "Chaviano would have dispatched a hit squad to the mines to put a bullet in my head. That man wasn't fond of people caught giving aid to the insurgents."

The G2 henchmen questioned Victor Daniels until very late that evening. At one point, Varona was asked by a soldier to step outside, apparently to take a phone call. When he returned, the G2 captain told Victor Daniels he was free to go home. Sleep-deprived and weary, he was brought back to the house by the same men who picked-him up earlier.

To everyone's relief, that was the last time the family heard from the ominous Captain Varona or the G2 for many years. Nick's father was convinced that his life had been spared thanks to Commander Faustino Perez' intervention on his behalf.

In his broadcasts on Radio Rebelde from the Sierra Maestra during the insurrection years and in the months thereafter, Castro promised to be an open-minded and benevolent ruler. However, the intimidation tactics, the psychological and physical tortures, and the summary executions perpetrated by his regime made Batista's henchmen pale in comparison. With no free press to keep the Communist government in check, Castro had *carte blanche* to retain and abuse his power using any means he pleased.

Victor Daniels believed the only hope left for Cuba was a violent overthrow of the regime by exile forces with the full support of the United States. The democratic government that Castro had promised for Cuba was beyond realization, mainly because the Communist dictator never intended to keep his word in the first place.

Castro would repeat his signature slogan one thousand times

over, "*Patria o Muerte*," country or death. Those words meant that Cuba would either remain communist under his uncontested rule or, in Castro's own words, *"become a barren land of smoldering ashes."*

Chapter 9

The greatest thing in the world
is to know how to belong to oneself.
— *Michel de Montaigne*

The disappearance of the market economy in Cuba forced scores of citizens to scramble for their survival. Thousands were leaving the country with just the clothes they had on to start a new life elsewhere. Others, with no place to go, had to put themselves at the mercy of the Communists in power. In no time, just about every able-bodied adult on the island was forced to work for the regime for practically nothing in return.

Nick's father had an alternative plan though. Summoning his entrepreneurial wits and business savvy, Victor Daniels pulled the formula of one of his inventions from a drawer and started manufacturing, in his own garage, a product the Cuban government could not refuse to buy.

Prior to receiving a degree in engineering from the University of Michigan, he and a fellow student had discovered an amazing chemical formula—a compound of sulfates that purportedly prolonged the life of lead-acid batteries commonly used in automobiles, trucks, tractors, and ships.

The engineer named the miracle product Ataflus-On, which spelled backwards read *no sulfata* in Spanish—meaning no sulfate. He claimed that the product slowed down the damaging buildup of sulfate crystals on the electrolyte cells, the main reason for the failure of lead-acid batteries. It wasn't long before the engineer swayed the regime to believe that his invention would save the country millions in hard currency over the years.

In 1961, Ataflus-On was the only privately manufactured product being sold to government enterprises in communist Cuba, and a lucrative source of revenue for the Nickolich family. Whether or not the compound worked as claimed was never proven beyond doubt, but the business flourished nonetheless. At one point, every single truck and tractor on the island had its batteries treated with the miracle powder manufactured and packaged in a private home in Siboney. The whole family eventually got involved in both the manufacturing process and in the packaging of the amazing crystals for distribution.

Nick attributed part of his father's success to a handful of decision makers in the government run institutions that bought and used his product. At the end of each month, the same faces would show up at their doorstep to collect their hefty padded envelopes. Even after the abolition of Capitalism, cash still moved mountains in Cuba.

The engineer found a novel way to become self sufficient and beat the food scarcity problem. The nonsensical agrarian reform law, along with the eradication of the free market system had put the Cuban economy into a nosedive. After decades of building a prosperous and self-sustaining domestic market, Cubans on the island now faced empty store shelves and were issued wartime food and clothing rationing cards. The regime had to import almost every basic article of necessity previously produced by the now defunct private industry.

The scarcity of food and consumer goods prompted Nick's father to turn his home's backyard into a productive farm. He planted new fruit trees around the house perimeter and began to grow every tropical vegetable he could find seeds for.

Soon enough, a variety of dissimilar creatures started to appear in their lavish gardens in Siboney. Rabbits, hens, chickens, and ducks began to roam freely all over the place. A family friend built a barn for the largest of all animals, a Holstein cow named *Rosita*, and a pigsty behind the shed that could house two full-grown swine at a time.

Meanwhile, *Long Tail*, the house cat, had been chased one time too many by an ill-tempered rooster. Fearing for his life, he never again ventured out to the backyard. The curious feline would sit for hours on the kitchen windowsill—staring in disbelief at the unfriendly creatures that had invaded his old roaming domains.

Nick was twelve or thirteen years old when his father appointed him farm hand, crop picker, handyman, barn cleaner, chicken slayer and *matador* of swine. He worked the farm every day like an adult after coming home from school. Before sacrificing the pigs, Nick had to gag the animals to prevent the grisly squeals from reaching the ears of a policeman, or of a snitch that could be passing near their house. Under the new laws, the slaughter of animals, or the interstate transport of meat by private citizens was a serious crime punishable with both fines and time in prison.

In spite of the looming threats, the illegal farming in Siboney thrived for many years. The family never lacked vegetables, meat, milk, homemade butter, yogurt and cheese, fresh eggs, and even homemade bars of laundry soap — items that were either tightly rationed, or had disappeared from the store shelves.

Any surplus was promptly traded for toothpaste, toilet paper, coffee and sugar, or was bartered to pay for the home visits from their family doctor. Victor Daniels did whatever was necessary to guarantee that his family never went to bed hungry.

But most importantly, he taught his children the most valuable lesson in life—to never give up.

Chapter 10

Defeat is not the worst of failures. Not to have tried is the true failure.
— *George Edward Woodberry*

Bay of Pigs, 1961

The sudden explosions sounded like the house next door had been blown to pieces. The intensity of the blasts made Nick's house shake to its foundations and all the glass windows rattle. Without thinking twice, the boy sprinted from the breakfast table and out to the backyard to look where the detonations had occurred.

Built on a sloping hill, his house offered a panoramic outlook of the main street and beyond. From the roof, the view stretched almost all the way to the ocean. The boy noticed a large cloud of black smoke rising rapidly on the eastern horizon. As he started to climb on the roof, two more thunderous blasts shook the ground. Awestruck, he watched more columns of black smoke going up about a mile away.

The two twin-engine planes suddenly came into view before he could actually hear them. Both planes were flying low above the ground and seemed to be headed straight for his house.

A quarter of a mile out, the two planes made a steep turn

turn toward the ocean and disappeared from sight with a deafening noise. Later in the day, the boy learned that the planes he saw flying toward his house were B-26 bombers conducting a surprise attack on the Libertad Air Base.

His father told everyone to run downstairs and take cover in the underground garage. Instead, the boy decided to hide behind the chimney. He didn't want to miss the amazing spectacle unfolding before his very eyes. From his vantage point, he watched the multiple anti-aircraft tracer rounds shooting up into the sky, followed by secondary explosions as black flak plumes popped-up above the clouds. The planes never returned, but the AA fire still went on for another half hour or so. The sight was out of this world.

That morning, Nick's father tuned in his Blaupunkt radio to the frequency of Radio Swan, a CIA operated radio station that transmitted into Cuba from an island off the coast of Honduras. Radio Swan reported that several air raids were taking place against major air bases in Cuba by defecting pilots from the Cuban air force.

The Cuban radio, however, gave a totally different account of the raids. While it confirmed that an undisclosed number of B-26 bombers took part in the sorties, it categorically denied that the airplanes belonged to the Cuban air force.

In reality, Radio Swan broadcasts had been part of a CIA plot to make believe that estranged Cuban pilots had conducted an attack on the Cuban bases to topple Castro's regime. The B-26 bombers had been painted with fake Cuban air force insignias and were piloted by both Cuban exiles and American pilots.

The preemptive sorties, which originated at CIA-operated airfields in Central America, were aimed at destroying all combat-ready aircraft at Libertad, San Antonio and Santiago de Cuba air bases. It was the prelude of a secret large-scale military invasion by exiled Cubans to overthrow Castro's regime. However, after the dust settled, several of Cuba's T-33s, B-26s, and Sea Furys remained undamaged and ready to fend-off the invasion.

A day later, on April 16, 1961, a Marine convoy sailed secretly from Puerto Limon in Nicaragua toward the swampy beaches of the Zapata Peninsula on the southern coast of Cuba. Four ships bearing the names Houston, Río Escondido, Caribe and Atlántico reached the shores of Playa Larga and Playa Girón at 2:00 hours EST. Aboard those vessels were nearly one thousand, four hundred Cuban exile troops from the 2506 Expeditionary Brigade, their weapons and all the support equipment.

At about 7:30 in the morning, several C-46 and C-54 transport aircraft dropped one hundred and seventy-seven paratroopers from the brigade's parachute battalion over several tactical spots near Playa Larga. The airborne troops' mission was to secure all roads leading to the main landing area of Playa Girón.

Planned by Dwight Eisenhower in March of 1960, and executed by John F. Kennedy a year later, the Bay of Pigs invasion was a disaster from the start. While many Cubans, both in the United States and on the island believed their liberation was at hand, the outcome would trigger unimaginable consequences for decades to come.

As usual, politics played a significant role in the military operation from its early beginnings. On the campaign trail for the presidency of the United States, John F. Kennedy often criticized what he called Eisenhower and Nixon's weak policies toward Castro's dictatorship. On October 19 1960, Kennedy's campaign released the following statement.

"We must attempt to strengthen the democratic anti-Castro forces in exile, and in Cuba itself, who offer eventual hope of overthrowing Castro. These fighters for freedom have had virtually no support from our government. We must act immediately to prevent communism from taking over other countries in Latin America by removing the conditions under which communism thrives. This week I outlined a twelve point program for accomplishing this, but thus far Mr. Nixon has been completely silent."

In that statement, Kennedy implied that he would act real tough on Cuba if he were to win the presidential election.

Prior to stepping down as president of the United States, General Dwight Eisenhower instructed Allen Dulles, then head of the CIA, to provide training and support to a few thousand Cuban exiles for a secret armed invasion of Cuba that would remove Castro from power. A team of experienced military strategist was called in to draft a plan and put it in motion.

On the day President Kennedy moved into the White House, however, his key advisors presented him with their own plan on how and where the invasion should take place. Kennedy went ahead and approved the changes.

Among the many deviations from Eisenhower's original strategy, the most damaging one was switching the landing site from Trinidad to Playa Girón, a remote beach in the inhospitable swamps of the Zapata Peninsula. Kennedy's advisors argued that landing a Cuban exile force near Trinidad, a city inhabited by nearly eighteen thousand people, could provoke a negative international backlash against the United States.

The men responsible for drafting the Trinidad plan strongly disagreed. U.S. Marine Colonel Jack Hawkins and CIA project director Jacob Esterline, both World War II veterans, had received intelligence that the people of Trinidad were highly opposed to Castro's regime. Their consensus was that landing the invasion near that city would ignite the spark that was needed for a mass popular uprising that could spread throughout the entire island. After landing and securing a beachhead, the Cuban exile forces also needed a suitable place to set up a provisional government and ask for recognition by the United States. Only Trinidad offered those conditions.

Another tactical consideration for choosing Trinidad was its close proximity to the Escambray, a rugged mountain range where thousands of guerrillas were already fighting against Castro's regime. If things went sour after the landing, the members of the 2506 Brigade could retreat to the Escambray and team up with the anti-Castro guerrilla network. Trinidad also had suitable beaches for a marine force landing and an airport that could be used as a forward base by B-26 bombers, C-47s transports and other support aircraft.

Richard Bissell, the CIA chief of operations during the Bay of Pigs invasion, reportedly warned Kennedy that landing the invasion at a location other than Trinidad would result in a fiasco. The White House went ahead with the changes regardless. The atmosphere in Washington, DC grew tenser by the minute as President Kennedy and the people close to him refused to listen to Bissell, Hawkins or Esterline.

In January 9, 1961, three months before the launching of the exile invasion, the news of an imminent military operation against Castro leaked to the press.

The article was written by Tad Szulk and printed in the New York Times under the title "U.S. helps train anti-Castro force at a secret base in Guatemala."

The planned invasion of Cuba by the Cuban exile forces was no longer a secret. Turner Catledge, the NYT's managing editor was greatly troubled by the security implications of Szulk's story. In Catledge's own words: "I could envision failure of the invasion and I could see the New York Times being blamed for a bloody fiasco."

Forewarned by the New York Times article, Castro had his troops ready and waiting. Immediately after the air raids of April 15, Castro's State Security police took steps to neutralize the internal resistance inside Cuba. The G2 rounded up more than one hundred thousand people suspected of being opposed to the regime and locked them inside several baseball stadiums, schools and prisons throughout the country.

Calling off the promised air support proved to be another catastrophic mistake. Fourteen hundred Cuban freedom fighters landed on the Zapata swamps without the air umbrella that Kennedy had promised. To make things worse, the White House recalled the additional B-26 sorties that were scheduled to fly to Cuba to destroy the combat airplanes that remained undamaged after the April 15 raids.

The invading forces found themselves in serious trouble the moment Castro's army gained control of the only road leading from Playa Larga to Jaguey Grande. Heavily outnumbered and without air support, the members of the 2506 Brigade became beleaguered by Castro's artillery and relentless air strafing. The men were forced to surrender less than seventy-two hours after landing in the swamps of Playa Larga and Playa Girón.

That morning, twelve A4D-2 Skyhawks from the U.S. Navy VA-34 Squadron, their insignias covered with gray paint, were launched by the USS Essex aircraft carrier group sailing off the southern shores of Cuba. The planes, armed with 20 mm cannons, were supposed to provide a defensive umbrella to the Cuban exile forces, and also to escort several B-26s that had taken off from a base in Nicaragua to conduct additional sorties inside Cuba.

The jet fighters circled idly over the fleet waiting to move into the theater of operations, but the orders to engage never arrived.

Frustrated, the U.S. Navy pilots watched helplessly as the transport ships and the men on the ground became sitting ducks for the surviving T-33s and Sea Furys from Cuba's air force. Flying in unchallenged skies, Castro's diminished—although still effective air force went on to strafe the invaders to a carnage end. By the end of that same day, the entire crew of the Essex carrier group was sworn to secrecy.

Whether the fourteen-hundred men of Cuban exile forces could have succeeded in creating a beachhead in southern Cuba and defeat Castro's two hundred thousand regular troops and militia still remains a subject of controversy.

Still, their chances for success were greatly reduced by several wrong decisions made by Kennedy and his closest advisors, and also by the reckless article published in the New York Times, which took away the secrecy of the operation.

THE LYNX

Operation Mongoose, 1961

In the aftermath of the Bay of Pigs fiasco, John F. Kennedy ordered Richard Helms, then head of the CIA, to remove Fidel Castro from power by way of covert operations inside the island. Under the name of Cuban Project, or Operation Mongoose, the CIA went on to wage a secret and costly war against Cuba that lasted until the mid-sixties. For this purpose, the agency opened a secret command and control center in the south campus of the University of Miami.

In all, Operation Mongoose reportedly had a much larger budget—approximately fifty-million dollars per year, and staff than any other CIA geographical directorate in the world, including the Soviet Union. General Edward Lansdale, a highly decorated intelligence officer who had served with the OSS during World War II, was put in charge of the top-secret operation.

During Operation Mongoose, an undisclosed number of paramilitary teams infiltrated Cuba to conduct covert missions and acts of sabotage against military, industrial and agriculture objectives. Scores of agents, most of them Cuban exiles, were killed, captured or turned into double agents during the life of the operation.

Kennedy's covert actions against Fidel Castro ended on November 22, 1963, the day the American president was tragically assassinated while riding in an open limousine in the streets of Dallas. To this day, the theory that Fidel Castro either knew about the murder plot, or played a covert role in Kennedy's assassination is still being speculated upon.

But before millions of people worldwide would mourn the loss of the charismatic American leader, a global crisis involving Cuba, the Soviet Union, and the United States—in its principal roles, would keep the world at the threshold of a nuclear cataclysm.

Chapter 11

Cuban Missile Crisis, October 1962

A few miles south of La Palma in Pinar del Rio, an unmarked fork on the road veers discreetly to the right behind a row of tall trees and a thick foliage overgrowth. The narrow road extends past a guardhouse, continuing westward for a few hundred yards to a loop in front of a contemporary ranch house with a swimming pool.

The beautiful ranch stands about six hundred feet from a rock promontory or *mogote* with nearly vertical walls and covered with dense vegetation—one of many that dot the stunning Sierra de Los Organos landscape. Those who have had the privilege to visit Finca San Andrés have sworn that the views from the ranch house are absolutely amazing.

Up until 1965, the lavish property was the home of Lawrence Lunt, his wife, and their three children. Lunt, a rancher from Wyoming, was also a U.S. Air Force veteran who had flown as radar navigator for a night fighter squadron in World War II, and later over the Sea of Japan during the Korean conflict.

In 1955, after receiving an honorable discharge from the armed services, Lunt was recruited by the CIA. The agency was in need for a resident operative and political analyst in the Caribbean and ordered Lunt to look for a permanent base of operations in the area.

In 1956, after searching in the Bahamas and the Greater Antilles, Lunt decided to purchase a few hundred acres of land in the Los Organos mountain range in western Cuba.

The deed on the *Finca San Andrés* was written in the name of Lunt's father-in-law, becoming the first Belgian owned property on the island. Lunt started building a cattle ranch on the property and settled in with his wife and their children. Lunt undertook cattle ranching with an utmost passion next to his covert work for the Central Intelligence Agency.

Lunt also rented a small apartment in Havana, a place he visited several times every month. It was where the American kept his CIA code books hidden inside a secret hole under the bathroom windowsill.

When Castro's forces seized the Cuban capital on January 1, 1959, Lunt was in an ideal spot to relay information back to the CIA on everything that transpired on the island. Soon, the agency instructed him to expand his contacts inside the diplomatic circles in Havana, and to build a spy network in Pinar del Rio by recruiting his most trusted farm hands.

In 1962, one of Lunt's operatives noticed a number of large crates being transported from the port of Mariel to a sisal farm near the town of San Cristobal. Lunt immediately relayed the information by radio to the U.S., prompting the CIA to send U2 spy planes on flights over Cuba to photograph the suspicious crates.

The images brought back by the U2s were shocking. They revealed that the Cubans had begun to erect launch sites for medium-range ballistic missiles (MRBMs) near San Cristobal, and what appeared to be Soviet medium-range missiles being transported on tractor trailers. It's now believed that the intelligence reports provided by Larry Lunt may have saved the world from a nuclear catastrophe.

Washington, DC. The Crisis

The following excerpts were taken from declassified transcripts of the Joint Chiefs of Staff meetings that took place in October of 1962, which show the gravity of the crisis that unfolded on the island of Cuba. These transcripts are a testimony of President John F. Kennedy's resolve in the face of a grave national danger. [1]

On October 16, 1962, in a Joint Chiefs of Staff meeting in the White House, the Defense Intelligence Agency presented the first photographic evidence of three SS-3 Soviet ballistic missile sites in Cuba taken by U2 spy planes. The aerial photographs revealed the presence of medium-range ballistic missiles—MCBRs—with a potential range of 700 to 1,100 miles that could be made operational within twenty-four hours.

At the briefing was General Maxwell Taylor, chairman of the Joint Chiefs of Staff, General Earle G. Wheeler, Army chief of staff, General Curtis E. LeMay, Air Force chief of staff, General David M. Shoup, commandant of the Marine Corps, Admiral W. Anderson, Chief of Naval Operations, and General Seth McKee, Air Force vice chief of Staff.

---

[1] Source: National Security Archive

The JCS agreed that once the offensive MRBM sites became operational, Castro could threaten retaliation for any offensive move by the United States. A delayed action until the missile sites were set up could touch off a nuclear war.

General Shoup pointed out that the Soviets could be attempting to pose a nuclear threat to the United States without running the risk of nuclear retaliation against the Soviet Union. The Joint Chiefs of Staff agreed that the threat was serious enough to require the United States to take out the missiles by military effort.

General Wheeler and Admiral Anderson recommended an air attack on the targets in Cuba followed by an invasion as the only way to remove the Communist regime from Cuba.

General Seth McKee said he foresaw the possibility to avoid the need for an invasion with the efficient application of air strikes, along with a naval blockade of the island. He stressed that the threat would be gone once the missiles and aircraft were knocked out, after which an invasion would not be necessary. General David Shoup, however, favored giving the Soviets an ultimatum to remove the missiles, or the United States would destroy them.

The JCS agreed to recommend the following sequence of actions to the president, gather additional intelligence and make surprise attacks on the missiles and missile sites, the surface-to-air missile sites—SAMs—, and tanks. At the same time, reinforce the defenses at the U.S. naval base in Guantanamo and lastly, initiate the invasion of Cuba.

After being debriefed at the White House by General Maxwell Taylor, the chairman of the JCS, President Kennedy gave unlimited authority to use U2 aircraft reconnaissance over the island.

On October 18, Defense Intelligence Agency officers presented the JCS with aerial photographs of four separate permanent MRBMs sites in Guanajay, San Julian, San Cristobal and Santa Cruz.[2]

The DIA analysts said it would take six months to make the sites fully operational. General Maxwell Taylor immediately expressed his deep concerns about permanent missile sites showing up in Cuba and stated that air strikes might not be enough. Occupation seemed to be the only possible answer.

Secretary of State Dean Rusk, who had initially opposed taking military action, conceded that the new information changed his outlook. He believed that action would have to be taken, and of a heavier kind than previously contemplated. However, Rusk believed that Soviet Premier Khrushchev should be informed in advance.

Kennedy said the United States should hold back until he got a feel for the Russian reaction. There would be an initial political approach, followed by a warning, a naval blockade, hitting the missiles, and an invasion-in that order.

At a White House briefing on October 19, the Defense Intelligence Agency informed the president that Cuba had thirty-five to thirty-nine MIG-21s, twenty-one IL-28 bombers—seventeen still in crates, seven MRBMs sites, four of which were for SS-4s with 1,000 nautical-mile range and three for SS-5s with 200 nautical-mile range. There were also sixteen launchers for the SS-4s and twelve for the SS-5s with two missiles each. Cuba also had twenty-two SAM sites, of which nine were believed to be operational. In weeks, those SAM sites would give the Cubans a couple of air defense nets with real capability against U.S. air strikes.

---

[2] Page 236

On Saturday, October 20th, the president said he might want to hit the missile sites as early as the next morning.

Kennedy asked General Maxwell to send a memo to all commanders involved that an operation against all offensive weapons and supporting defenses in Cuba could be launched as early as October 23th or 24th. The JCS agreed.

That same day, General William Michael of the Defense Intelligence Agency informed Kennedy that an emplacement for the 1,020-nautical-mile range medium-range ballistic missiles were now operational near San Cristobal. Each site had eight missiles and four launchers. Another emplacement, this one for the much longer range MRBMs, had been photographed near Sagua la Grande and could be operational within six weeks.

After a long deliberation, the Pentagon proposed a five-day blockade followed by a strike. Meanwhile, General Taylor expressed serious concerns that if they waited to hit the missiles, Cuba and the Soviets would have time to hide them.

A final decision was made to implement a naval blockade of the island of Cuba by U.S. Navy ships to take effect twenty-four hours after the president's TV speech. Procedures were to be added later in the week. The United States would be prepared to execute a surprise air strike against the missiles on October 22 or 23, or after giving a twenty-four-hour notice.

Kennedy stated that he didn't want a Pearl Harbor on the American record, and also have a chance to protect unprepared allies against Soviet retaliation. There were talks about possible negotiations with the Soviets about giving up the Jupiter missiles based in Turkey and Italy, which could be replaced with Polaris subs in the Mediterranean Sea.

Confronted by the imminent threat that the Soviet missiles

posed to the United States, President John F. Kennedy ordered the naval quarantine of the island of Cuba. The United States called the Soviets and demanded the immediate withdrawal of the offensive MRBMs from Cuba, and the dismantlement of all the rocket launch sites. The chilling standoff would later be known as the Cuban Missile Crisis.

Twelve hours earlier, Admiral Robert Dennison, the commander in chief of the Atlantic Command—CINCLANT— had begun positioning U.S. Navy ships at a centralized rendezvous point in the Caribbean and had sent detailed orders for conducting the quarantine of Cuba to all commanders involved. The initial surface quarantine line was set at five hundred miles from Cape Maisí in Cuba to keep the U.S. ships out of range of the Soviet IL-28 bombers.

The outcome was two quarantine circles, each with a five hundred-mile radius, within which Soviet and other bloc ships would be interdicted.

On October 26, Castro lost his nerve. Fearing an inevitable invasion by the United States, Fidel ordered his security detail to drive him to the Soviet Embassy in Havana. In the presence of Soviet ambassador Alexander Alekseyev, Castro dictated an encrypted letter to Khrushchev, the premier of the Soviet Union, in which he urged the launching of a nuclear missile attack against the United States if the Americans were to invade Cuba.

That same evening in Moscow, Premier Nikita Khrushchev wrestled with an extremely serious situation. U.S. Navy ships had surrounded Cuba and President Kennedy appeared determined to strike the missile sites and land U.S. Marines if the missiles were not returned to the U.S.S.R. immediately.

Castro's impulsiveness became a great concern to his bosses at the Kremlin. The Cuban leader was acting like an irresponsible maniac who could easily provoke a nuclear catastrophe if left unrestrained. Khrushchev knew he needed to act fast. Having witnessed firsthand the horrors of World War II, the Soviet premier decided he wasn't about to allow a nuclear holocaust to happen over the island of Cuba.

Khrushchev would soon be proven right about Castro's ill temperament. On October 27, the Cuban dictator fired a SA-2 surface to air missile and shot down an unarmed U2 plane flying a reconnaissance mission over Cuba. The U2 pilot, USAF Lieutenant Rudolph Anderson, was killed when the exploding shrapnel punctured his flight suit and caused it to decompress at high altitude. [4]

On October 28, after receiving a pledge from President Kennedy not to invade the island, Nikita Khrushchev ordered the missiles dismantled and shipped back to the U.S.S.R. In a separate accord, the United States agreed to withdraw its Jupiter missiles from Turkey and Italy, which the Soviet Union regarded as offensive.

It took more than three years for the Cuban counterintelligence services to uncover Larry Lunt's spy network and place the American under arrest. After months of harsh interrogations, first at the G2 headquarters in Havana, and later on at the prison of La Cabaña, Lunt was sentenced by a mock tribunal to serve thirty years in prison. The CIA operative would spend the next fourteen years of his life in several Cuban jails under extremely inhumane conditions.

---

[4] Page 237

On September 17, 1979, Lunt and three other Americans jailed in Cuba were exchanged for a group of Puerto Rican terrorists who had carried on an armed assault on the U.S. House of Representatives back in 1954.

Lunt's beautiful *Finca San Andrés* near La Palma, also known as *La Casa del Americano*—the Americans' house, was confiscated from his family and became one of the many grand homes reserved by Fidel Castro for his own leisure in his private island of Cuba.

Rumor has it that the famed Colombian surrealist writer Gabriel Garcia Marquez, a close friend of Castro, wrote two of his novels while living as Castro's guest at the *Finca San Andrés.*

THE LYNX

Chapter 12

The Cold War had become a battlefield marked by doublespeak. Disguise,
distortion, and deception was accepted as reality.
— *Annie Jacobsen*

Nick spent a good part of an hour to complete the multi-page application to join the skydiving club. While most questions were political in nature, the very first one dealt with a seemingly unrelated subject.

Do you believe in God?

The people of Cuba had long been forced to adopt atheism as their way of life, therefore an affirmative answer would have automatically doomed the application to the trash can. There was no room for people of faith in the Communist realm.

The parachute club wanted to know everything about the applicant's track record in the Communist Party or the Communist Youth, participation in volunteer work drives and other absurdities the regime gave top importance to.

Nick was asked to write down the names of all his relatives and friends living outside Cuba, and how often he corresponded with them. With the splintering of the Cuban society going on for over a decade, almost everyone on the island had either a friend, or a family member living in exile, or both.

Nonetheless, Castro expected all his subjects to break ties with those whom he regarded as "worms subservient to the Yankee imperialism." The Marxist revolution, Castro said, was above any blood ties or friendship bonds.

There wasn't much about his life that he cared to share with the government. He decided to answer most of the general questions with half-truths, and leave others intentionally blank. He had never joined any social or political organization, or spent a minute of his life doing volunteer work for the regime. On more specific issues like whether or not he had relatives or friends living in the United States, Nick just lied.

Chances were that the club would not have enough resources to conduct a thorough background check on every single applicant, or the time to do so effectively. With an outdated and unreliable telephone system on the island, such checks would require sending someone to go and knock on doors while getting around on public transportation. The verification of every single candidate's credentials would be a daunting and improbable task.

His military service record worried him, though. The skydiving club would never accept a candidate who had received a psychiatric discharge from the military after allegedly engaging in a firefight with space aliens.

Nick decided to take a gamble. He wrote down that he had served his full term as a medic at a base in Pinar de Rio. Four years had gone by since he was released from the army. He could bet, with a certain degree of certainty, that his military records were collecting dust inside some file cabinet at the Ministry of the Armed Forces. He said a short prayer, signed the application and handed it over to the woman at the front desk.

"Did you bring your letters of reference comrade?" the

secretary asked.

"I didn't know I had to."

"We will need a letter from your place of employment, and one each from two different political organizations." The woman was reading over his application when Nick noticed a frown appearing on her face.

"I see that you are not a member of the Communist Youth."

"No, not yet." Nick answered.

"That's not a determining factor if you have other credentials. We will consider your application if you bring us three letters of recommendation—one from your place of work, one from the labor union and one from the CDR."

"I'll get you those letters right away," Nick said, not sure of how he could ever comply with that requirement.

"Great. I'll need the letters here within a week if you want to get on the list for the next physical exam. If you miss the deadline, you will have to wait a few months before the next opportunity opens up. My name is Ana Maria. If I'm not here, you can leave the papers on my desk."

"Thank you Ana Maria. I will be back in a day or two."

Nick's boss in the linguistics department didn't hesitate to write him a good recommendation letter, but the other documents he needed would have to be forged. He could not get references from the labor union simply because he had never been part of that organization. The CDR membership posed a similar problem. He'd never set foot in such a place. It was time to get creative.

CDR is the Spanish acronym for Committees for the Defense of the Revolution. Franchised on every street block in every city in Cuba, the CDRs were dens of snitches that keep detailed tabs on every family in their city block, and duly reported every suspicious activity to the secret police. Mirroring the police state regimes of Eastern Europe, Castro instituted the CDRs to spy on every single person living on the island. They were his eyes and ears in the city streets, rural towns and mountain passes of Cuba.

Nick didn't know of any CDR operating in the vicinity of his home. Almost everyone living within five or six blocks of his house was a foreign diplomat, a *Mayimbe*, or a student enrolled at a nearby boarding school.

A bit of detective work got him the address of a house about two miles from his home that apparently functioned as a CDR. The place, he was told, was run by a woman from Oriente named Leticia. He decided to pay Leticia a visit that same evening.

Leticia lived in a beautiful modern house, one of the many in Siboney abandoned by families forced into exile. Hers happened to be one of the nicest in her block, making Nick suspect the woman might enjoy the rewarding of some higher up in Castro's government. The lady who answered the door was stunningly beautiful.

"I'm Leticia. What can I do for you?"

Nick introduced himself and told the woman he had wanted to join the CDR for many years.

"I've never been approached by anyone from the CDRs. It was only after asking around for a while that I got your address."

"My son and I just moved here from Santiago last December," said the lady. "There are only two other people in our small organization. We would love to have you as a member. Please come in."

Leticia offered him an armchair in her elegant living room and served him Cuban coffee and homemade biscuits.

"Leticia, I must confess that I'm in a bind and need a big favor from you. I have just applied to join the skydiving club, but they want a letter of reference from the CDR. I hate to put you on the spot, but do you think you can write a letter stating that I've been a member of this CDR since it opened its doors?"

The woman looked at him straight in the eye for a few seconds and then smiled.

"So you want to be a parachutist? I would love to help you out. It wasn't your fault that the organization never reached out to you."

The alluring CDR president went above and beyond what Nick had asked. Leticia wrote him a long letter of recommendation in which she described his participation in the CDR as months of dedicated tenure to the cause of the revolution. There were still nice people left in Cuba and Leticia was definitely one of them.

Two letters down, one more to go.

Nick brought home a few sheets of official stationery from the university and went to work. Using his father's aging Underwood typewriter, he wrote a letter stating he was a member in good standing of the worker's union. The letter also read that he had completed over one hundred volunteer work hours in that year. The end result was an official looking document the club officials should accept without reservations. He signed it at the bottom of the page forging the signature of the labor union's secretary.

One day before the deadline Nick brought all three letters to Ana Maria.

"Thank you, comrade. I will call you personally if you get selected for an interview."

Ana Maria stapled the letters together and placed them in a manila folder with Nick's name written on it. He walked out of the office with his fingers crossed, hoping that no one would try to verify the authenticity of one letter in particular.

Two days later, Nick's mother had news for him when he returned home from work.

"A woman named Ana Maria called today. She said you have an appointment at the aviation club tomorrow afternoon at four thirty. What is that all about?" his mother asked.

"Mom, I applied to become a glider pilot," he lied. Nick wanted to keep from his mother that he intended to jump out of airplanes and spare her the additional stress. He could always tell her about skydiving later on.

If he got accepted at the club and succeeded in taking a jump plane to the United States, there was the risk that the Cuban regime could turn their rage against his parents. But he didn't think Castro would dare to inflict them physical harm, or hold them back for too long. They were both advanced in years and lived in an expensive property coveted by several people in Castro's inner circles. His parent's beautiful home in Siboney could someday become their ticket out of Cuba.

Nick showed-up at the club's office at four-fifteen the following day. He found Ana Maria at her desk filing her fingernails.

"You are right on time," she said. "The head of the skydiving club will see you now."

The secretary ushered him into an oval shaped office at the back of the colonial house. The scantily furnished room had a medium size wooden desk, two chairs, and a gray metal filing cabinet in the far corner of the black and white checker-tiled floor. Two old parachute packs and a polished pair of jump boots had been stacked against another wall. Ana Maria asked him to step inside and then closed the door behind her.

Moments later, another door opened at the other side of the

high-ceiling room from where a rough looking, middle-aged man made a stately entrance. The *apparition* wore tight olive-green pilot coveralls a size too small for his potbellied frame, zippered black aviator's boots, and a .45 Cal pistol tucked at the waist. The man listed noticeably to one side, making Nick wonder if that was the result of a not so gentle landing in his past.

"I'm Lieutenant Medin Rosabal, chief parachute instructor. Please have a seat."

Medin Rosabal spoke with the typical vocal intonation of the people born and raised deep in the mountains of Oriente. Medin was a true *Oriental* from head to toe.

The head of the parachute club sat at the other side of the desk and pulled a stack of papers from a folder. He started reading in silence, looking up at Nick from time to time. It was the application Nick had filled out a few days earlier, along with the letters of reference he had brought to Ana Maria.

Medin got up and went to pace around the room, all while uttering an emotional monologue about his underprivileged origins. He had grown up in a wood and straw house on a coffee plantation in the mountains, a place that taught him the meaning of hard work at a very young age. One day, Castro's rebels showed up at his *Bohio* and made him join the guerrilla when he was only fourteen years old. By the time the rebel forces made their way to Havana, Medin had reached the rank of lieutenant in the rebel army.

In the years that followed, the young lieutenant was commissioned to pioneer a Special Forces airborne unit attached to the Ministry of Interior. A few years later, he and a few other officers were sent to the Soviet Republic of Armenia to receive advanced parachute training.

Back from the U.S.S.R., Medin was discharged from the military and tasked with creating the first civilian parachute club on the island. However, the pistol at his waist indicated that the man's ties with the Ministry of Interior had not been totally severed.

"Your last name is Nickolich. It sounds Russian. Is it Russian?"

"No comrade, my family name is Yugoslavian."

"So your father is Yugoslavian?"

"Yes. He's from that part of the world—the country of the great *Marshall Tito*."

Touché. Lince knew had to keep from Medin, at all cost, that his father was American. Admitting to that fact would have raised a flag and likely cost him his admission in the parachute club. His Montenegrin heritage had offered him a most opportune cover. Since Yugoslavia was a communist country friendly to Cuba, it would be great if Medin believed he was a direct descendant of a native Yugoslavian.

"It says on your application that you work as an English translator at the University. What made you decide to study English in the first place?"

"Ever since I was a young boy, I've been fascinated with foreign languages. I intend to enroll again in language school at night, this time to study both Russian and German."

Nick needed a good excuse for his knowledge of English. Many fanatics in Cuba believed that the folks who studied English did it because they wished to immigrate to the United States.

He kept his answers to an absolute minimum. When Medin asked him about his school background, he skipped the years spent at the private Catholic military academy. That alone would have branded him as a *petit bourgeoisie* in the eyes of the commissar. He also kept from Medin that he had been expelled from a public school accused of spewing subversive enemy propaganda in class.

There were many other aspects of his life that Medin didn't

need to know. Like most youngsters in Cuba, he loved American and British pop music. The head of the parachute club would have paled at the fact that certain atmospheric conditions determined which American radio stations, thousands of Cuban men and women listened to in the seclusion of their homes.

Nick was a fervent listener of WQAM, a top-forty station from Miami that came to the island with great clarity from the early morning hours until dusk. After dark, another radio station, KAAY, came with amazing sharpness from a distant city called Little Rock in Arkansas. It would be impossible for a hard-core communist commissar from Oriente, dressed in a tight pilot's suit and packing a .45 Cal pistol, to understand why so many people on the island were so deeply contaminated with Western values.

"Comrade, we could definitely use your language skills. We are having issues with our new Czech sport parachutes. I think we have been packing them incorrectly. The instruction manuals came in English." Medin said.

"It will be my pleasure to translate those manuals for you, comrade. The textbooks I work with daily at the university are probably boring in comparison."

"You wrote on your application that you served as a medic in the army. Did you pick up any other skills while in the military?"

"Besides breaking down, oiling and firing infantry weapons, I spent most of my time in a field hospital dispensing aspirin, giving penicillin shots and stitching up minor wounds. I wish I had seen some combat action, though."

"I think you will make a good skydiver, Comrade Nickolich. If you pass the physical exam I will not object for you to join our club."

"Thank you. I can't wait to make my first jump."

Nick walked out of Medin's office with a smile on his face. Had his offer to translate the Czech parachute manuals swayed the man's decision in his favor? Whatever his reason might have been, the head of the Cuban parachute club had just given a member of the passive underground resistance the green light to infiltrate his cloistered realm.

The twenty or so men gathered outside the military hospital that morning did not apply to the elite MIG fighter pilot school. However, the physical requirements to become a parachutist in Cuba were nearly the same. Oddly enough, the first order of the day was to put everyone's inhibitions to the test.

"Take off all your clothes and put them in this bag," ordered a good- looking nurse, handing them a burlap sack each. When everyone had stripped to the skin, she asked the men to follow her on a seemingly endless hallway. There were scores of doctors, nurses and medical students going about their business, all pretending the naked men were not there. Another nurse was waiting at the other end of the corridor to hand them their examination gowns.

After donating three large vials of blood at the lab, the men got ushered through several specialist offices in a conveyor belt fashion. They were put through pulmonary capacity tests; chest x-rays; orthopedic evaluations; ear, nose, and throat inspections; prostate and genital exams; and a thorough check of their eyes and general vision.

At the psychiatrist's office, Nick was puzzled by a large black fly that was perched on top of the doctor's bald head. He chose to ignore it.

At the end of the day, all the men gathered at the hospital's parking lot to talk about their experiences. Everyone had seen the odd fly on the shrink's head and concurred it was a fake. Word came later, however, that those who tried to be funny and made a remark about the fly, or laughed about it did not pass the physical.

A week later, Ana Maria left a message at his home. Medin wanted to see him immediately. When Nick arrived at the office, the look in the man's face told him the news was not good.

"I'm sorry, Comrade Nickolich. The results of the physical exam just came back and unfortunately you were disqualified. The orthopedist report states that you suffer from a lumbar scoliosis, meaning that your spine is not straight. It says that your back will not tolerate the impact of a parachute landing."

"Comrade Medin, I can assure you there is nothing wrong with my back," Nick protested.

Medin stood silent for a moment.

"On the other hand, there might be a way around this. I may be able to override the hospital's decision if another orthopedic doctor certifies in writing that you are fit for parachute jumping."

That same day, Nick looked up the address of an orthopedic specialist in the phone book and went to have his back examined. After a brief exam, and fifty pesos later, the physician signed a letter certifying that parachute jumping would not affect his slight lumbar condition. He rushed back to Medin's office brandishing the paper as if it were a prize trophy. Medin read the letter and gave Nick a pat on the shoulder.

"Congratulations, comrade. I like people who don't give up. I will see that your name gets put on the list for the next jump course."

THE LYNX

Chapter 13

They always say time changes things,
but you actually have to change them yourself.

— *Andy Warhol*

"Michael, do you remember our last trip to Ariguanabo? The time we saw the skydivers landing at Cayo la Rosa?" Nick asked.

He had invited Michael for a drink in his backyard, one of the few places where they could talk freely without fear of being overheard, or recorded. He knew the DSE had microphones planted all over Michael's property.

"Of course, how can I forget? The bloody jumpers scared our ducks away."

"Well, I already had a talk with the guy in charge of the skydiving operations, passed the physical exam and was approved to join the club."

"Congratulations. I'm very happy you made it in."

"To be honest, I feel like I've stepped into a den of wolves. If those guys ever find out about my true intentions, they will not hesitate to tear me to pieces."

"I'm sure you will survive. Watch what you say, though. What you don't tell them cannot incriminate you—don't forget that nobody can read your mind. And under no circumstances ever share your secret with anyone, not even with your best friend. Make that your golden rule."

"Thank you, Michael. I will take heed of your advice. As you can understand, I can no longer be seen in the company of foreigners, or even stay in touch with my sister and other relatives in the USA. I would not be surprised if the secret police starts running spot checks on me."

"That you can count on, Nick. Good luck."

"It's been a real pleasure getting to know you and Annabel, and spending such great time in your company. I sincerely hope you get to publish your article in National Geographic."

After five long weeks of intensive training, Nick's group was ready. The trainees had completed the required physical conditioning and taken classes on parachute packing, canopy maneuvering, and emergencies. Lastly, the group went to Libertad air base to practice parachute landing falls, or PLFs, on a zip line from a thirty-four foot tower. That was their final test before the actual jump from an airplane.

At the break of dawn on February 1st, 1972, Nick arrived at Cayo la Rosa to make his first parachute jump. It was a beautiful, cloudless day in Lake Ariguanabo with a gentle breeze blowing from the east. He was just nineteen-years-old.

The jumpmaster for the day was Basilio, a burly African-Cuban who had doubled as their physical trainer and packing instructor throughout ground school. Basilio had lined-up their main and reserve parachutes, coveralls, their jump boots and a helmet on top of an old canvas tarp. Nick noticed the parachute packs had long lost their original color and had multiple tears and holes on them, probably from being dragged over mud and rocks too many times. He hoped the canopies inside were in better shape.

As the jumpers geared up, another instructor stepped in to perform a visual check of their equipment. It was Collazo, the same guy who had greeted him and Michael Quinn at the airport gate a few weeks earlier. Collazo didn't seem to recognize him.

"You guinea pigs are good to go," Collazo said with a chuckle. "You'll be test jumping some old parachutes that our resident rigger patched-up last week."

Nobody laughed.

Basilio led the jumpers to a waiting helicopter—an olive drab Russian MI-4 with Cuban Air Force markings. The chopper had been brought in from San Antonio Air force base to replace the club's AN-2 plane which was undergoing maintenance for the day.

As the men stepped inside the chopper, Basilio hooked up the static lines to a steel wire stretched above their heads—the system that would open their parachutes automatically upon exiting the aircraft.

From his bucket seat across the open door, Nick watched the ground getting smaller in a dimension he didn't know existed. The only time he had flown in an aircraft before was in his father's single-engine Beechcraft when he was seven years old.

The droning of the chopper's engine, along with the cool wind that brought in a whiff of high-octane fumes, suffused his senses. The experience reminded him the military drops in movies—only that this time it was him flying in an aging Russian helicopter and about to jump out. The adrenaline rush he felt at that moment was much too real to ignore. Nick shrugged off a momentary feeling of unease and focused on performing the jump exactly as he had been taught.

At twelve hundred feet above ground, Basilio gave the command for the jumpers to stand up and run out the door at three-second intervals. Nick recalled those first seconds as a total blur. He felt a tug on his shoulders and watched a large, off-white parachute slowly deploying above his head.

Down below him, a flock of Mallard ducks flew in perfect formation over the glimmering waters of the lake. He thought of Michael Quinn, who would have given anything for that amazing sight alone. Much too soon, his Russian PD-47 parachute glided him gently toward the grass runway and set him down on his feet. At that moment, all he wanted was to get back aboard the chopper and do it all over again.

In the weeks and months that followed, the drop zone at Cayo la Rosa became Nick's second home, and also his best kept secret. It would be unwise to advertise he had become involved in skydiving. Someone from his past could snitch on him to Medin, or to another instructor at the club.

In stark contrast, most of the regular jumpers at Cayo la Rosa were intractable communists. Some of the elders, like Lieutenant Medin Rosabal, were veterans of the Sierra Maestra insurrection, or the Escambray campaign. Others often bragged of having participated in covert operations overseas. In all, most of the people there seemed to have played some kind of active role during, or after Castro's rebel war.

However, it didn't take long for the young rookie with the Slavic surname to blend in with the gang. He loved skydiving and didn't mind spending time with his new and dissimilar group of friends. It was a brotherhood like no other he'd ever belonged to.

Every so often, Nick would go for a late afternoon stroll on the grass runway at Cayo la Rosa. If he got lucky, he would get to watch one or two Russian TU-95 long-range bombers on a low approach to the San Antonio Air Base to the south of the drop zone. They were the same planes he had first noticed while hiking around the lake with Michael Quinn.

The VOA had once aired an interesting report about the TU-95s unusual flights to Cuba. After taking off from their base in central Russia, the planes followed an elaborate route along the coasts of Norway, the United Kingdom, Iceland, Greenland, and then skimmed the eastern seaboard of the United States before landing in San Antonio. The Americans suspected that those planes were packed with highly sophisticated signals intelligence equipment and were indeed conducting spy missions as they flew near the U.S. mainland.

The VOA had also identified the primary role of the TU-95 advanced strategic bombers as capable of delivering nuclear payloads anywhere in the world.

As with every other sport in Cuba, the regime had placed considerable resources to subsidize and run the parachute operation in Cayo la Rosa. The USSR and Czechoslovakia had supplied the club with parachutes, boots, helmets, altimeters and rigging equipment. The jumpers could make as many jumps as they wanted, restricted only by their skill level, the weather, or by how fast they could repack their parachutes. The jumps were free, and so were the equipment, the food, the lodging and the shuttle service to and from the drop zone. There were always one or two AN-2 aircraft available for the jump activities, several pilots on call and an unlimited supply of gasoline. Castro's friends in the Kremlin had deep pockets and seemed eager to give him just about everything needed to build a competitive sport parachute club in Cuba.

Nick made good his promise to translate the manuals for the Czech-made parachutes. As Medin had suspected, the cause of the frequent malfunctions was an oversight in the packing sequence.

His help with the manuals earned him some clout with the club instructors. He was soon allowed to trade his military-style parachute for a steerable sport rig and given the green light to perform free-fall jumps from nine thousand feet—a privilege reserved then for a select group of jumpers. One skydive at a time, Nick started making headway in the fast-growing sport.

The jumpers also enjoyed a rather controversial perk at the drop zone. It was an off-limits cafeteria reserved exclusively for skydivers and pilots. Three times per day, they were served dishes that had long disappeared from the average Cuban kitchen. The menu included beefsteak, pork chops, ham, fish, cheeses, milk, yoghurt, rice, bean soups, vegetables, fruits and desserts, all at no charge.

"Every athlete undergoing strenuous training in Cuba needs an adequate food diet. The same goes for the pilots," an instructor told Nick.

Nick viewed those privileges as a contradiction to the hyped social equality preached by Castro and his cronies. In his eyes, nobody on the island should be deprived of an adequate nutrition. The rationing of basic food products imposed on the general population was a travesty in a country that had prided itself for being self-sufficient for decades. This proved, once again, that

Castro's socioeconomic system was a failure.

Ultimately, the regime did so to get credit for the athletes' performance at international events. Castro had a visceral need to show the world that his regime was capable of producing top-rated competitors in nearly every sport, even if the rest of the population went to bed hungry. It was all about selling his big communist lie abroad.

In 1972, Nick was part of a group of skydivers to receive a sporting license from the parachute club. The licenses provided them a paid leave of absence from work, along with free room and board in the drop zone. For three months, the jumpers underwent an intensive training program in all the parachuting disciplines. Rumors had it that Cuba intended to participate in international skydiving competitions in the not so distant future.

By mid 1973, the government extended the license privileges indefinitely to a few of the top performers. Nick was part of the small group chosen to skydive year round.

By then, Nick had given up the idea of hijacking a jump plane to the United States. The primary reason had to do with fuel. From day one, he noticed the jump planes were met at the runway by the gas truck after every other landing. A close inspection of the cockpit fuel gauges showed the tanks were never filled to more than one fifth of their capacity. That practice reduced the AN-2s range to less than one hundred miles and rendered the aircraft incapable of reaching the United States.

But other factors would also come to play in his decision. Even with enough fuel on board to fly across the Florida Straits, it would be difficult to persuade a jump pilot to fly him to the United States. To force someone to take such action against his will was not in Nick's nature and therefore out of the equation.

Now recognized as one of the top skydivers on the island, Nick realized he might have a chance to be selected to the national team and sent to compete abroad. If he got lucky, he could find himself in a foreign country and running for his freedom. Over time, many Cuban athletes had defected while attending sporting competitions abroad. Maybe someday he would have a chance to do the same.

Chapter 14

The skydiver counted four unmarked Alfa-Romeo sedans parked outside the drop zone at Cayo la Rosa. The shiny vehicles were equipped with long communications antennas, a giveaway they belonged to the secret police. The presence of DSE operatives at the airfield that early in the morning could only mean that something serious had occurred. As the shuttle van drove through the front gates, Nick noticed a dozen of uniformed officers talking to a few of the instructors and pilots by the airport's main building.

"The airplane used for towing the gliders is gone," one of the instructors told Nick.

The theft of the Piper Pawnee had been well planned and brilliantly executed. Two men had stolen the plane just before sunrise and flown it to the United States.[5] It had been an amazing feat, but one that Nick feared could provoke a political purge at the drop zone. The episode could easily prompt the DSE to conduct a thorough review of the security measures at the parachute club, or

---

[5] Page 237

demand a reevaluation of everyone's political credentials. It could also mean the end of Nick's skydiving career.

At about ten that morning, the intelligence officers summoned all the skydivers and glider pilots to an emergency meeting.

"The men who took the Piper Pawnee are paid agents and saboteurs at the service of the CIA," one of the officers declared. "All the parachutes in the storage room must be checked thoroughly for potential acid damage. But most importantly, not a word of this incident shall be spoken outside this airport. We cannot allow the enemies of the revolution to use today's incident for their propaganda purposes," the officer added.

After unpacking and inspecting every parachute in storage, the skydivers concluded that none of the rigs had been tampered with. The allegation that the men who took the Piper had used acid to sabotage the gear was another dirty trick to smear the character of the men who just wanted to be free.

The men responsible for the caper were Julian, the Piper's mechanic, and his brother Ricardo. That night, Julian had been on scheduled guard duty at the airport and was the only one present at the facility, which made it uncomplicated for him to get his brother inside.

The escape was carried out with military precision. Julian and Ricardo cut the phone lines, disabled the radio communication equipment, and topped the gas tanks of the two-seater Piper using the gas truck. Just before sunrise, the brothers pushed the airplane to the end of the grass runway, fired up the engine and took off.

Some residents at Cayo la Rosa recalled hearing an airplane taking off just before dawn, but nothing after that. Because neither man was a pilot, the DSE assumed that Julian had learned the basics of flying during his mechanical check rides in the Pawnee's back seat. It was a plausible theory since that particular plane was relatively easy to fly.

The Voice of Americas radio brought the news two days later. It reported that two brothers from Cuba had taken off in a small airplane and ditched it next to a U.S. Coast Guard cutter near the Florida Keys. Both men were rescued unharmed and granted political asylum in the United States.

Julian, as Nick remembered him, was as a friendly guy who was always willing to lend a hand. It was obvious that neither Julian nor his brother were at the service of the CIA or other foreign intelligence service, but rather two courageous men who had seized the moment and claimed their right to be free. He felt a great admiration for the brothers and wished that someday he would have the opportunity to do something similar.

Fortunately, at least that time around the DSE did not take retribution against the skydivers who were not members of the Communist Party, as Nick had feared might happen. The incident, however, was a reminder that his cover could get blown in a blink of an eye.

The inland key of Cayo la Rosa[6] had a fascinating history. In 1931, a Long Island entrepreneur named Dayton Hedges signed a long term lease with the Cuban government and developed what would become one of the largest textile manufacturing complexes in the western hemisphere.

The employees at Textilera Ariguanabo knew Dayton as a fair man who had great respect for those who worked for him. Besides

---

[6] Page 238

the cotton-spinning factory, Dayton built a modern residential neighborhood, a fire department, a baseball field, an infirmary, a day care facility, a small printing office and a state- of-the-art grass runway outfitted with automated landing lights.

Built at the edge of Lake Ariguanabo, the runway had a sophisticated drainage system that kept the ever-changing water levels of the lake from flooding it. After Castro's regime seized the textile complex, the small airfield was converted into an air base for Russian AN-2 crop dusters. The airfield was also used as a pilot training facility for a select group of people in the regime's top hierarchy.

"Ché Guevara took one of his first flying lessons at this airport in a Piper PA-18, and in a Cessna 182 nicknamed *Lobito—young wolf.* His flight instructor was an air force Captain named Eliseo De la Campa," a Cayo la Rosa resident had told Nick.

Captain De la Campa was a frequent visitor at the airfield, where he kept a red Piper PA-18 sheltered in a small hangar. The veteran pilot would show up almost every weekend to either work on the small Piper Cub, or take it for leisure flights over the island.

Every so often, Lince would spot a single-engine Piper Cherokee practicing takeoffs and landings at Cayo la Rosa. He identified some of the people taking the flight lessons as top civilian and military personalities from Castro's inner circle.

The flight instructor was Richard Harwood Pearce, a former U.S. Air Force major and Viet-Nam veteran who had defected to Cuba in 1967. Pierce, who had just lost custody of his son after a bitter divorce, took the young boy with him on a Cessna 150 for the ninety-mile journey from Key West to Cuba. Because U.S. radar installations on the Southern border were trained to look for incoming flights only, Pierce was able to fly his single-engine plane to Cuba undetected.

Chapter 15

Fifty kilometers south of the Port of Batabanó lay the Isle of Pines, the inspiration for classic books such as Treasure Island and Peter Pan. Castro later renamed it as the Isle of Youth. To this day, however, most people still call the island by its original name.

Early in the twentieth century, the Isle of Pines gained notoriety after the construction of a maximum-security jail near the capital city of Nueva Gerona. The complex of circular buildings was completed in 1925 using the same design as the Joliet penal facility in Illinois. Prior to 1959, Presidio Modelo had hosted a wide diversity of criminals inside its thick concrete walls, including Fidel and Raul Castro Ruz, two physically dissimilar brothers from the small town of Birán in Oriente.

How the Castro's ended-up in that remote prison can be traced back to one of the darkest episodes in Cuba's history. In 1956, Batista's army had Fidel Castro cornered after the ill-fated attack on the Moncada barracks in Santiago de Cuba. After a failed attempt to seize the military garrison, Fidel and some of his followers fled from the scene and went into hiding. With the Cuban military intelligence in hot pursuit and no place to run, Castro reached out to Monsignor Enrique Perez Serrantes for help. He asked Serrantes to demand an assurance from both President Batista, and from the army's commander in Santiago that his life would be spared if he were to surrender.

Perez Serrantes, then the archbishop of Santiago, handed Castro over to the military authorities after Batista promised the insurgents a fair trial. However, the charges brought against the rebels were very serious indeed. Fifteen enlisted soldiers and three policemen had been killed during the scrimmage, while twenty-three others were wounded—some of them critically. Nine of Castro's followers also died in the operation, and eleven were wounded—four of them allegedly by friendly fire.

A few days after Castro surrendered, an army patrol found a young man wandering on a railroad track near the small town of San Luis. The man gave himself up and lied about his identity. When taken into custody, he eventually confessed that his name was Raul Castro—Fidel's younger brother. Raul admitted to having participated in the attack to the Moncada garrison, but blamed his brother for planning and leading the failed military operation.

A graduate attorney, Fidel Castro took over his own defense at the civil trial that took place in Santiago de Cuba. During the trial, Castro gave a long speech that he ended with the words "history will absolve me."

Not many people realized then that those were the exact same words used by Adolph Hitler during his defense at the *Rathaus Putsh* trial in Munich in March of 1924. Some of Castro's classmates at the University of Havana recalled that *Mein Kampf*, the autobiographical manifesto of Adolph Hitler, was one of Castro's favorite books during his years in law school.

The evidence presented by the prosecution was overwhelming. At the end of the trial, the judge sentenced Fidel and his collaborators to fifteen years in the maximum security prison of

Presidio Modelo on the Isle of Pines.

On May 15, 1951, after serving less than two years of their sentence, Castro and his followers were released from jail as part of a general amnesty granted by President Batista. Unfortunately for tens of thousands of Cubans, both Fidel and Raul Castro forgot the meaning of the words amnesty or pardon the moment they walked out of jail.

Ten years later Castro would repay the favor granted to him by Monsignor Perez Serrantes and the Catholic Church in a grand fashion. On September 1961, the secret police rounded up more than one hundred priests from cities and small towns all over the island and shipped them to Spain aboard the steamer Covadonga. They were told to never come back.

In the months that followed, Catholics, Protestants and Jews watched in dismay nthe padlocking of the temples of worship. The church of Saint Thomas of Villanova, located a few blocks from Nick's home in Siboney, was turned into a warehouse for fine works of art looted from the homes of wealthy Cubans gone into exile. Many other churches were also put to similar use.

Between 1962 and 1963, the Cuban government brought in several art experts to sort and catalogue the booty. Hundreds of porcelain vases, oil paintings, Persian rugs, marble sculptures and many other works of art worth millions of dollars were crated and shipped secretly out of the country. The loot was eventually sold anonymously at auction houses worldwide.

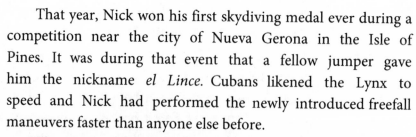

That year, Nick won his first skydiving medal ever during a competition near the city of Nueva Gerona in the Isle of Pines. It was during that event that a fellow jumper gave him the nickname *el Lince*. Cubans likened the Lynx to speed and Nick had performed the newly introduced freefall maneuvers faster than anyone else before.

The man who taught him the new skydiving modality was Viacheslav Jarikov, a cheerful Russian instructor with gold teeth nicknamed *Slava*. Slava had been hired to train the top Cuban jumpers in advanced competition skills, and also asked to select the members for the first Cuban national parachute team. Cuba had recently joined the FAI, the International Aeronautical Federation, and made a pledge to send a team to the XII World Parachuting Championships in Szolnok, Hungary. At the end of the evaluation camp, Slava chose Lince as one of the five skydivers to represent Cuba in the upcoming event.

Although Lince was Slava's top pick for the team, the young man feared he would become a victim of political bias and get sidelined. The regime usually precluded athletes who were not members of a Communist organization from traveling to competitions abroad.

The last word on whether or not he could be part of the team now rested in the hands of the State Security Directorate. Lince's only qualifications were his undisputed skydiving skills, and the powerful nomination by the Russian instructor. He didn't believe that would be enough, though.

The officer responsible for signing off on the travel permits was Tony Angulo, a lieutenant from the Cuban counterintelligence services. Nick had known Angulo from the days he started skydiving at Cayo la Rosa. The taciturn lieutenant would often show up impromptu at the wheel of his VW Beetle, always dressed in a well-pressed olive drab uniform, shiny black boots, and a 9 mm Makarov pistol in a waist holster. Angulo's unannounced visits to the drop zone induced fear in just about every pilot, mechanic and skydiver. Lince never saw the man crack a smile.

The reason for the collective paranoia was not unfounded. Lieutenant Angulo's job was to keep an up-to-date dossier on every person involved in the parachuting and gliding operations. The officer knew everything about everyone's past and present life and had unlimited powers to decide who could stay and who must go.

It was now up to Angulo to conduct a thorough background check of Slava's picks for the national team and determine who would be attending the World Meet in Hungary. Lince feared that if Angulo dug much deeper into his past, he might stumble into his military service record, or find the damaging letter from the school he had been expelled from a few years back.

Days after the selection camp ended, Lince was summoned to the dreaded meeting with Lieutenant Angulo and Bienvenido Garcia, the director of the Cuban Air Sports Institute. At the closed-door meeting, the intelligence officer questioned Lince extensively about his past life and particularly about his relationship with his sister in the United States. Angulo had obviously completed all the background checks, but there was no way of telling how much the man actually knew.

Much to Lince's relief, the intelligence officer didn't bring up his expulsion from school, or his alleged firefight with Solarian aliens at the army base in Pinar del Rio. Perhaps his past political sins had been swept under the rug in consideration for his competitive skills. However, that was something that Lince would never get to know.

"You will be notified of our final decision in the next few days," the DSE officer told him.

A week later, Bienvenido called Lince with the good news.

"Congratulations, Nick. We believe that you will be a great asset to the national skydiving team. The training camp for the competition in Hungary starts in two weeks."

Two years after joining the club, Lince had surmounted a seemingly improbable obstacle—getting permission to travel outside Cuba. He thanked Bienvenido, whom he believed had interceded on his behalf. However, he knew that the regime's decision had likely been influenced by geopolitics. Hungary was still another communist country with closed borders to the free world.

In any case, there might still be a chance to jump ship on his way to Hungary. Their flight to Europe included two refueling stops, one in Gander, Canada and the second at Barajas airport in Madrid. Lince made a mental note to keep his eyes wide open and his legs ready to sprint.

Chapter 16

The crepuscular light flooded the Czech Airlines Il-62 cabin with alluring shades of gold, giving it a surreal appearance. Lince stepped inside the aircraft and found his assigned seat by the window behind the bulkhead. His travel companion was no other than his friend Bienvenido, the head of the skydiving delegation to Hungary.

In his late thirties, the director of the Cuban air sports institute was slim, intelligent and soft-spoken. The man had risen in the party ranks when, at a very young age, he was sent to fight against the anti-communist forces in the Escambray Mountains. While Lince secretly opposed Bienvenido's political views, he respected the man for his fairness and positive disposition in life. Lince also understood the importance of having someone with Bienvenido's political clout on his side.

Many years later, while dying of cancer and being scolded by his own son for not allowing him to leave Cuba, Bienvenido wondered if he had done the right thing by following Castro's doctrine blindly. Among his multiple overseas assignments, he served as Cuban ambassador to Canada, and lastly as ambassador to Sana'a in Yemen before falling seriously ill and being forced to return to the island.

Days before his death, Bienvenido would whisper a shocking revelation to an old friend visiting from Argentina.

"I don't know if I did the right thing after all," he confessed to his friend with visible regret.

Bienvenido's singular career in the Cuban intelligence services dated back to the sixties, when a very powerful man took him under his wing. His godfather of sorts was General Manuel *Redbeard* Piñeiro, one of Castro's most trusted commanders. Piñeiro attended Columbia University in New York, married an American-born professional ballerina and returned to Cuba to help organize Castro's urban guerrilla movement. Piñeiro was detained briefly in Havana by Batista's security police and then fled to the mountains of Oriente to join the insurgent war.

A few years after Castro's victory, Piñeiro founded the Directorate of General Intelligence or DGI, Cuba's counterpart to the CIA. His two top intelligence advisors at the time were Markus Wolf, the top man in the dreaded East German Stasi, and Vladimir Semichastny, the feared head of the Soviet KGB.

However, Piñeiro's stellar creation during his career as head of Castro's intelligence services was the National Liberation Department, later renamed Department Americas, or DA. With an unlimited budget and vast human resources at its disposal, the DA became the most devious and secretive organization in Castro's Cuba.

Working hand in hand with the Kremlin bosses and the KGB, the DA embarked on a covert, long-term effort to destabilize and overthrow democratic governments throughout Latin America. The DA's ultimate goal, however, was to penetrate and destroy the core of the American establishment.

Over the years, the DA managed to infiltrate moles and sleepers at all levels of local and federal governments, fund socialist political campaigns and candidates, bribe and influence labor union leaders and recruit members of the American academia.

Most of the DA's covert operations were carried out by diplomats operating from Cuba's embassies and consular offices worldwide—and by agents functioning as illegals in target countries where Cuba didn't have a diplomatic presence, like in the United States.

Lince suspected all along that Bienvenido Garcia had been a ranking officer in the DA for quite some time. However, his friend never brought up his work, or politics. Bienvenido, on the other hand, knew that Lince had never been active in Cuba's political scenario, but never questioned the skydiver's motives. Perhaps he believed that he was destined to turn the young man's mind around.

The Ilyushin IL-62 reached V1 speed and lifted off the ground toward the North Atlantic. After a five-hour flight over the eastern seaboard of the United States, the plane landed to refuel in Newfoundland. As the aircraft came to a halt, Bienvenido stepped into the aisle to address the members of the skydiving delegation.

"We need to stay close together in the holding area. If anyone needs to use the restroom, please use the airplane's lavatory before getting off."

The IL-62 passengers deplaned in Gander under a light drizzle, where two spirited Czech flight attendants brought them inside the terminal building. Lince was the first one in his group to enter the secure holding area and took a seat next to a double glass door connecting to the main terminal. The door was guarded by an officer from the Royal Canadian Mounted Police.

Lince felt tempted to open the door and ask the Canadian

officer for political asylum. If he found the door locked, he could always bang on the glass and draw the officer's attention. However, he wasn't sure that his appeal for help would be well received in that country. Back in Cuba, he overheard one of the instructors at Cayo la Rosa talking about a Cuban artist who had been denied political asylum in Canada and forced back to the island in handcuffs. Lince couldn't tell if the instructor's story was true or, if the man had tried to plant a seed of doubt among those traveling with the team through Canada. He decided the risk wasn't worth the taking.

The IL-62 landed in Madrid at dawn on the following day for the last refueling stop before heading off to Prague. The airplane came to a halt next to one of the terminal buildings, where a flight attendant announced that the stop would be brief and the passengers needed not to deplane. Still, the airplane door was opened and rolling steps brought in for the pilots to go outside.

"My leg muscles are totally cramped. I would like to go out for a short walk," Lince told Bienvenido.

Bienvenido gave Lince a puzzled look, but said it was okay for him to step outside. However, he asked one of Lince's teammates to go with him.

"It's not safe for you to go outside alone," Bienvenido told him. The skydiver chosen by Bienvenido to accompany Lince to the airport building was Francisco Quintino, call sign *Tucán*—a man to be mindful of. Tucán was a burly paramedic with the Cuban Red Cross who held a black belt in Judo. Moments later, Lince took down the airplane stairs to the tarmac with his teammate following on his heels. It was a cool and dry summer morning in Madrid.

In 1973, Tucán had been part of the fifteen hundred Cuban soldiers sent by Castro to fight along several Arab nations in the Middle East war. The Arab attack on Israel took place during Yom

Kippur, the holiest day in Judaism. While in Syria, Tucán had probably acquired enough combat skills to complicate matters for just about anyone on the team, including Lince.

The airport gate in Barajas was deserted but for two relaxed men tending a small liquor stand. Lince and Tucán approached the bar and asked the men for a glass of water. Lince had hoped to find a Spanish policeman, or a customs agent in the gate area whom he could ask for help. As for the relaxed bartenders, he guessed the men would never intervene on his behalf if they saw him involved in a scuffle with Tucán.

The gate area was connected to the main terminal by a long and unlit corridor. Lince's first impulse was to take off sprinting down the hallway and try to find help at the terminal. However, he wasn't sure he could outrun Tucán, or find a policeman before he was forced to get back on the plane.

To complicate matters even further, Spanish dictator Francisco Franco enjoyed a friendly relationship with Castro. It would be very unlikely for Franco to engage in a sparring match with Cuba over a defecting athlete.

"I think it's time to get back on the plane," Tucán said. Lince finished his water, thanked the bartenders and walked out of the terminal followed by Tucán. As he climbed up the stairs back to the IL-62 Lince wondered if he had gotten too complacent, but conceded it was not his time. Not yet.

THE LYNX

Chapter 17

Freedom is never more than one generation away from extinction.
We didn't pass it to our children in the bloodstream.
It must be fought for, protected,
and handed on for them to do the same.

— *Ronald Reagan*

XII World Parachuting Championships Szolnok,
Hungary

In 1974, a seemingly unbridgeable chasm divided the world
into two irreconcilable philosophies. While most western nations
upheld freedom as the highest of human values, the Soviet Union
and its satellite regimes brutally repressed those who dared to
dissent from the Marxist-Leninist ideology. The cold war between
the free world and the Communist bloc was at its peak, augmented
by a dizzying buildup of both conventional and nuclear arsenals. In
spite of the ongoing political madness, the general atmosphere of
the world parachuting meet was one of peaceful coexistence and
friendship.

For nine consecutive days, the virtual barriers that kept the
world divided came crashing down under the skies of Hungary.
Skydivers from Russia, the United States, the Netherlands, Poland,

Cuba, East Germany and other countries sat side by side in the AN-2 jump planes and MI-8 helicopters, dined together and slept under the same roof.

The top parachutists of the world had convened in Szolnok to demonstrate their individual and team skills in free-fall acrobatics, and to score dead-center landings on the sand pit. It was the Olympic games of skydiving.

One of the highlights in Szolnok was the debut of Jalbert's Parafoil, one of the first wing-like parachutes to be jumped at a world-class competition. The pilot, a jumper from the USA team, scored almost six consecutive dead centers in the individual accuracy event under variable wind conditions.

While conventional round parachutes landed on the target downwind and with forward speed, the Parafoil wing approached the target upwind to a near midair stop before touching down. Lince believed the Russians would try to copy the Parafoil design, although the U.S.S.R. was far behind the USA in the manufacture of low porosity, light synthetic fabrics needed in the wing-like parachute construction. In any case, the era of round sport parachutes was nearing its end.

Up to that year, the two dominant events in the world of competitive skydiving were known as style and accuracy. Style involved jumping from an aircraft at seven thousand feet above ground level and performing a series of opposite, 360-degree flat turns in free fall, with one back loop between every two turns. The series was clocked from start to finish by a team of judges watching from the ground with powerful binoculars. Accuracy, on the other hand, was the art of landing on or as near as possible a four-inch disc placed at the center of a large sand pit.

Yet another discipline had developed at a very fast pace in the western world. It was known as relative work, or formation skydiving. While the style-and-accuracy world meet was taking place in Szolnok, the second world cup of formation relative work had just ended in South Africa. A team from the United States had won the gold in the competition held in Pretoria by linking ten men in free fall in a record time of 12.7 seconds from a DC-3 aircraft.

On their way back to the United States, the champion USA relative work team, *Wings of Orange,* made a surprise stop in Szolnok and performed an amazing demo jump. On that day, the incredible free fall skills demonstrated by the Americans virtually turned the style and accuracy world upside down.

After the American team landed, Lince asked permission from Bienvenido to speak to the captain and find out more about the novel skydiving discipline. He wanted to learn all about body flying, aircraft exit techniques and other details so he could put together a relative work team upon their return home.

The captain of the USA team was a friendly guy eager to demonstrate on the ground everything that Lince asked him for. Lince committed the valuable tips to memory and thanked the American for his advice. The skydiver's name was Jerry Bird, a pioneer in the art of freefall relative work and a living legend in the United States.

Bienvenido welcomed Lince's initiative for the sake of learning something novel, but two of his teammates thought that his conversation with Bird had been inappropriate. The men were Guerra and Urbano, two Communist radicals and sworn antagonists of everything American. They argued that if the Cuban jumpers were to learn something new in skydiving, they had to learn it from the Russians first. The men even suggested that the Soviets would be offended if Cuba were to engage in a new discipline ahead of them, or without their tutelage.

When the discussion started to turn sour, Lince decided to walked away. Those two radicalized fanatics had the political power to make his life extremely difficult upon his return to Cuba. They could even get him expelled from the sport.

Bienvenido concurred with Lince that formation skydiving could someday be a dominant event in world-class parachuting competitions. He asked the skydiver to write down everything he had learned from Jerry Bird so one day he could help train the Cuban team in that discipline. He agreed with Lince that Guerra and Urbano could make trouble for him and suggested that it would be better to wait until the conditions were right before bringing up the subject again.

While in Szolnok, Lince met a talented Australian free-fall photographer who had just published a beautiful pictorial book on skydiving. The photographer was Andy Keech and his amazing book was titled "Skies Call". Andy wrote down Lince's address and promised to mail him a copy of the book to Cuba.

At the end of the event, Lince learned he had scored in the top third combined overall ranking in the world and way ahead of all his teammates. Needless to say, that such achievement alone would help him secure a slot in the next Cuban national team.

The following day, the skydivers loaded their luggage and parachute gear in their van and headed off to Prague for a day of sightseeing before flying back home. While admiring the *Orloj*, a medieval astronomical clock in Prague's old town square, Lince found himself alone among a crowd of foreign tourists. He had been accidentally separated from his teammates.

While those circumstances could have facilitated his escape in a free country, it was of no use to him in Czechoslovakia. Like in

Cuba, the Czechs lived under communism and had their borders closed to the free world. After searching for his teammates for a good fifteen minutes, Lince decided to take a taxi to the airport. He hardly made it to the gate on time to board his flight back to Cuba.

The skydiver fell sound asleep shortly after takeoff and didn't wake up until an hour before the plane landed in Havana. Before crossing the Atlantic, the Cubana IL-62 had made a refueling stop on the island of Santa Maria de Azores, something that Lince had no recollection of. He had always been a light sleeper, thus he suspected that someone had slipped a sedative in his soda before the plane took off from Prague.

That year, Lince retained his supremacy at the Cuban parachuting nationals by winning once again the overall skydiving champion title. During a speech at the competition's closing ceremony, Bienvenido announced that Cuba would be participating in the Pan American Games in Peru in the spring of 1975. The head of the Cuban Air Sports club then added even better news. A four man free fall event had been included in the Pan American competition schedule. Bienvenido didn't wait to commission Lince to coach the team in relative work using the techniques he learned from Jerry Bird in Hungary.

A few weeks later, the mailman dropped-off a surprising package by his front door. It was the copy of the book Skies Call that Andy Keech had promised him back in Szolnok.

The book had amazing pictures of free fall formations that he could now use as an aid to teach himself, and his teammates the art of relative work. Keech's exceptional contribution to the sport of skydiving had found its way into the farthest corners of the world, including the prison island of Cuba. [7]

Not long thereafter, Kymbe and Lince would become the first two men on the island to hold hands in free fall while falling at one-hundred and twenty miles per hour over the inland key of Cayo la Rosa.

---

[7] Page 238

Chapter 18

Appearances are a glimpse of the unseen.
— *Anaxagoras*

III Pan American Skydiving Championships Peru,
1975

The skydiving team landed in Lima constrained by the typical mélange of stern rules imposed on all Cuban athletes sent to compete overseas. Prior to leaving Havana, the jumpers had received a thorough briefing by the DSE on what they were and were not supposed to say or do while in Peru.

As usual, the secret police orders were stringent. The skydivers had to stay in groups of two and more at all times, were not allowed to make phone calls, take a taxi or any form of public transportation, or accept gifts from strangers. They were expected to respond with physical force to any insults to Castro, or to the revolution. Lieutenant Angulo had told them the rules were to protect them from a possible aggression by Cuban exile groups or CIA agents. However, the skydivers knew better. Angulo wanted to minimize any contact between the skydivers and people of the free world and prevent a potential defection.

The team's security was stepped up that time around with the addition of two covert agents. The one who acted like the boss was Benitez, a reticent man who registered at the event as an observer for the Cuban Aeronautical Institute. The other was Yolanda, an inscrutable woman with cropped black hair and an ever-present 35mm Nikon camera slinging from her neck. Yolanda entered the event posing as a reporter for Deportes magazine. Yolanda would room together with Neri Garcia, the team's only female skydiver. Bienvenido was appointed once again as the leader of the skydiving delegation.

Lince made a mental note to keep both Benitez and Yolanda within sight at all times. The DSE agents had likely received extensive tracking and surveillance training and would be watching the skydivers day and night. Chances were that the pair had smuggled their 9mm handguns into Peru and would not hesitate to use them to stop a defector in his tracks.

The Pan American Games coincided with the start of the winter season in the southern hemisphere. In the early hours of the morning, a seamless cloud would roll in from the Pacific Ocean and settle deep into the valley floor. The milky cover would stay obscuring the sky until midday, the time when the sun eventually burned it off. That pattern had replicated itself every single day for the duration of the competition. The strange seasonal phenomenon was known by the locals as *la garúa*.

The team arrived mid morning at the Colón, a hotel in Miraflores booked for them in advance by the event organizers. While they all waited for their rooms to be ready, Lince walked up to the bar and ordered an *Inca Cola*. He wanted to try the local carbonated drink he had seen advertised on a billboard on their way to the hotel

"Is this your first time at the Colón?" the bartender asked.

"Yes, this is actually my first time in Lima. It's a very nice city."

"Welcome *amigo*. Yes, Lima is indeed a beautiful city, but you should exercise great caution here. We have had riots and street disturbances in the past few weeks."

"What's going on?"

"Things have been crazy in Peru for a long time. Actually, our problems started back in 1968 when a junta of generals seized power. Our elected president was forced into exile and Congress was shut down."

"A coup d'état?"

"That's what the newspapers called it. Seven years later, we still have General Juan Velasco Alvarado and his friends at the helm of the country. Peru has since become a close ally of the U.S.S.R. and Cuba.

"However, Velasco is now facing a massive popular discontent and has grown afraid of his own generals. Hundreds of armed soldiers have been deployed throughout the city to keep the situation under control," the man whispered.

Lince didn't know what to say. Obviously, the bartender had no clue he was with the Cuban team. He had on a skydiving tee shirt from the world meet in Hungary, but nothing that would have revealed his nationality. By sheer accident, he had received an enlightening exposé of the country's political state of affairs.

The skydiver suddenly realized that he could get in serious trouble if someone from his team overheard him talking politics with a Peruvian dissident. He thanked the man, paid for his soda and walked away.

The information Lince had received that afternoon had been extremely valuable, though. He would have to reconsider his original plan of seeking political asylum in Peru. Nothing back in Cuba had clued him on how far to the left the government of Peru had actually gone. If he made one false move, the regime of Velasco Alvarado would hand him over to the Cuban embassy without giving it a second thought.

There had to be another viable way to get out of Peru, he thought to himself.

According to Bienvenido, the appointment of Antonio Nuñez Jimenez as Cuban ambassador to Lima had not been accidental. Nuñez, a former captain in Castro's insurgent army and a founder of Cuba's Communist Party, was one of Fidel's most trusted "intellectual" collaborators. Castro had decided to send a man with extensive political experience to Peru in a frantic attempt to try and save the failing regime of Velasco Alvarado.

For nearly a decade, Cuba and the Soviet Union had made significant investments in resources and manpower to convert Peru into a satellite of the U.S.S.R. The military junta of General Velasco had received millions of dollars in small arms, artillery, tanks, armored vehicles, helicopters and combat aircraft.

While the Kremlin supplied the Andean nation with money and hardware, Cuba provided the military and political advisors. But now Velasco's internal political crisis had both Moscow and Havana wondering. They were very worried that their hefty investments in Peru could crash at any moment.

On the morning of the team's arrival in Lima, Nuñez summoned Bienvenido to an urgent meeting at the Cuban embassy. He asked the head of the skydiving delegation to collect everyone's passports and bring them to the embassy for safekeeping. Nuñez also wanted to discuss the contingency plans in case of an emergency. From a political standpoint, Peru was like a pressure cooker about to blow up.

Nuñez also told Bienvenido that the skydiving delegation would have to move out of the Hotel Colón. The team's new accommodations would be at the Alcazar, a smaller inn located near the city's center where most Cuban delegations visiting Lima were lodged.

Lima woke the next morning to *la garúa* in its full expression. The dense fog had seeped deep into the valley of the Rimac River and limited the visibility to less than one hundred feet.

The bartender had told the truth about the heavy military presence in the city. In the midst of the fog, Lince noticed rifle-toting soldiers in nearly every major intersection of the city, along with tanks and BTRs—Russian-built amphibious armored vehicles. Lima looked like a city under siege.

On the way out of the city, their van passed near a Renaissance mansion flying a foreign flag on the second floor balcony. A coat of arms on the compound's outer wall read *Embajada de Chile*— Chilean Embassy. The two iron gates that gave access to the compound had been blocked by identical armored BTRs along with half dozen soldiers in full riot gear.

That chancy discovery was troubling. Lince would have to forget about breaking into a foreign embassy to seek political asylum. The regime of Velasco Alvarado had not left any doors open for dissidents or potential defectors to leave the country in a hurry.

One last alternative would be to cross the border with Chile at a place known as *Linea de la Concordia*. But that idea posed some serious hurdles. The border outpost was almost eight hundred miles from Lima, about a twenty-hour drive on a long and winding coastal highway. Lince would first need to break through the DSE's surveillance net weaved around the team and then find transportation to reach the outpost before the authorities could find him.

Even if he could get that far, Lince would need some kind of fake ID to show at the border control on the Peruvian side. He didn't have to worry about Chile, though. A sworn enemy of Peru's communist regime, the government of Chile would welcome a Cuban defector with open arms.

Perhaps he could ask someone locally to help him out, but how could he tell who was, or wasn't sympathetic to Velasco Alvarado's regime? If he made the mistake of confiding in the wrong person, he could wind up in the hands of the Peruvian police. Lince thought about the friendly bartender at the Hotel Colón and made a mental note to look him up later on that evening.

The airport in Collique had served as a training base for the Peruvian air force until 1974, when a magnitude 8.1 earthquake destroyed most of its facilities. One section of a very large building on the airfield had escaped damage and was enabled as overnight gear storage for the participating teams. For shelter from the heat during the day, each team was provided a small tent pitched in a grass field between the runway and the taxiway.

The tents were marked with a wooden stake bearing the country's name and lined up in alphabetical order. Nine parachute teams had entered the event—Argentina, Brazil, Mexico, Chile, Cuba, the United States, Uruguay, Costa Rica, and the host country of Peru. The United States team, spelled *Estados Unidos* in Spanish, had their tent pitched next to the Cubans.

After the first day of skydiving in Collique, the team was taken straight to their new hotel in Lima, the Alcazar. To their surprise, they found out that personnel from the Cuban Embassy had already transferred all their belongings from the Hotel Colón into their new rooms. Ambassador Nuñez Jimenez' diligence had trashed the skydiver's plans to make contact again with the friendly bartender at the Colón.

Lince weighed his options to escape from the Alcazar during the night, but found it would not be an easy task. First, he was sharing a room with Tucán, the same guy who shadowed him in Madrid a year earlier. Second, Benitez and Yolanda, the two DGI agents embedded in the team, had taken rooms across from one another next to the elevator. From their vantage position, the agents could monitor everyone's comings and goings on that floor.

To complicate things, the hotel did not have a back door exit. Any guest wanting to come into the hotel after eleven at night, or leave that late for any reason would have to ring the bell and ask the concierge to let them through the front door. It would be impossible to leave the building in the middle of the night without someone knowing about it.

Because Ambassador Nuñez Jimenez had been personally involved in the hotel swap, Lince could safely assume that some employees at the Alcazar were on the Cuban Embassy payroll, and particularly those working in the evening shift. The Alcazar had become the team's virtual jail in the middle of Lima.

The ghastly screams of a woman got Lince on his feet and sprinting out of the food tent where he was having lunch. He noticed that Jake Brake, one of the guys from the U.S. Army team, had also left his lunch on the table and was following on his heels.

Not far ahead from the food tent was the area used by the skydivers to board the jump aircraft. Lince noticed a commotion next to one of the planes and saw its propeller coming to a halt. In a second's time, the pilot opened the door and literally dove out of the plane toward a young woman who had fallen on her knees under the aircraft wing. The man grabbed the woman under her shoulders and tried to lift her up, but her legs kept giving out. Lince hastened his pace to offer help, but was stopped in his tracks by another pilot who urged him to stay back.

On the asphalt under the airplane's wing was the young woman's arm, severed just below the shoulder. Jake and Lince stared at each other in disbelief. The men watched as the paramedics strapped the young woman onto a stretcher and rushed her to a small Bell 47 helicopter with a doctor running by her side. One of the paramedics had packed her arm in a bag with dry ice and brought it to the helicopter. The others proceeded to attach the stretcher to the helicopter right landing skid.

The medics stepped back and gave a thumbs-up signal. After revving the engine, the pilot eased the Bell 47 slowly off the blacktop, tipped the nose down and headed off to the distant mountains north of Lima. From his spot on the tarmac, Lince could see the doctor leaning precariously out the open door from his seat in the helicopter. The physician had the young woman's subclavian artery clamped shut with his bare fingers to stop the bleeding and to prevent it from retracting. Lince kept his eyes on the MEDVAC helicopter until the aircraft was but a tiny dot on the horizon. He prayed in silence that the woman would make it to the hospital alive.

"She is the Cessna's pilot's girlfriend," uttered a man in mechanic coveralls standing next to Jake and Lince.

"Apparently, she didn't see the halo of the spinning propeller and ran straight into it," the mechanic added. "The same exact thing happened to another woman last year, also on Good Friday. That woman was here earlier today."

"What a terrible misfortune," Jake uttered.

Earlier that day, Lince had indeed noticed a pretty young woman with a missing arm standing in the spectator's area. The thought alone that a similar accident had happened twice, one year apart and on Good Friday, made him shiver. Later on he would learn that the woman had survived, but the doctors were unable to reattach her arm.

Lince suddenly realized that he and Jake were alone and that there was no one from his delegation within sight. He had met Jake at the world competition in Hungary. Maybe the American wouldn't mind doing him a favor.

"How is everything, Jake?"

"Doing okay so far, thanks."

"Jake, can I ask you to do something for me?"

"Nick, that's no problem at all. What is it?"

"I have a sister in the United States with whom I have not spoken in years. The Cuban government has forbidden us to communicate with family and friends residing outside Cuba."

"That's regrettable. I'm sorry."

"It sure is. If the regime there finds out that I have talked to her on the phone or sent her a letter, I'll be kicked out of the skydiving team. The Secret police reads every piece of mail that goes in and out of Cuba. I wonder if you wouldn't mind writing her a brief note on my behalf when you get back home. I don't want my sister to think that I don't love her."

"I'll be happy to do that for you, Nick. What would you like me to tell her?"

"Just that I still love her and the reason why I can't talk to her anymore when she calls home."

"I will do that gladly. But I will need her address."

"I'll look for a way to give it to you in the next day or two. As you can imagine, I can get in serious trouble if I'm seen talking to you, or handing you a note."

"Of course. I promise to be careful."

"One more thing, Jake. How would you like to own a Russian altimeter? I brought along a spare one that I would like to trade you for a pair of skydiving goggles."

Jake smiled. "Nick, an altimeter is way too expensive. I'll be happy to give you the goggles for free."

"That's nonsense. The Russians just shipped us a crate full of them last month. You must accept it as a souvenir."

"Thanks Nick. I'll bring my spare goggles tomorrow. I'll think of a way to give them to you without getting you in trouble," he chuckled.

As the men stepped back into the lunch tent, Lince caught something from the corner of his eye that felt like a punch to his stomach. Standing in the middle of the field was Yolanda, the embedded DSE agent. The woman had the zoom lens of her 35 mm

Nikon camera pointed straight at him.

The next day, Lince was repacking his parachute by the team's tent when he noticed one of the Golden Knights heading in his direction. It was Captain Chuck Whittle, the leader of the U.S. Army team. Chuck had in his hand what appeared to be a black cotton bag.

"Nick, I would like you to check out a new deployment system that should work great with your UT-15 parachute. It's called the D-Bag and replaces the deployment sleeve. It makes the packing volume a lot smaller and also enhances a more gradual and softer opening sequence. I can install it in your rig if you don't mind trying it."

"Sure, that sounds great. But I first need permission from my team leader."

Lince didn't have to wait long. Bienvenido and Benitez had noticed Chuck Whittle and Lince talking in the packing area and had started heading their way. Two jumpers from Brazil had stopped by and stood watching, probably curious about what the American and the Cuban were doing.

"Bienvenido, Captain Whittle would like me to try a new deployment device on my rig. It's the same system they use on their parachutes," Lince told him.

"If you think it's safe to do so, I will not object," Bienvenido conceded.

"I think it's worth the try."

Under different circumstances, the head of the Cuban delegation would have been hesitant to allow one of his skydivers to jump his parachute with a modification performed by an officer in the U.S. Army. But Bienvenido was a class act and a born diplomat. To refuse Captain Whittle's gesture of goodwill would have made him look impolite in everyone else's eyes, including Agildo Vieira and Caribe Monte Santos, the two Brazilian skydivers who were still watching the unusual encounter with utmost interest.

"My team leader said it's okay."

"Great. I'll go ahead and pack it for you. Just so you know, I'm a certified parachute rigger in the U.S. Army."

Displaying exceptional rigging skills, the Golden Knight Captain quickly removed the deployment sleeve from Lince's parachute and replaced it with the D-Bag. He then shoved the folded parachute into the bag in an accordion-style pattern, stowed the lines into the rubber bands and closed the pack. [8]

"Your rig is all set to go. You will notice a more gradual and softer deployment of the parachute. I can't wait to hear what you think of it."

By that time, Jake had also joined the group. He had a pair of U.S. Army skydiving goggles dangling from his right hand.

"Nick, I noticed you don't have free-fall goggles. Please accept this pair as a gift. I swear they'll save your eyesight in the long run."

"Thanks, Jake. You really didn't have to do that, but I really appreciate it." Lince looked up at Bienvenido and shrugged. Jake had played his role flawlessly.

On the next jump, Lince went up with a pack on his back that looked more like a pillowcase with a large bump than a parachute. Chuck's D-Bag was intended for a parachute pack three times smaller than that of his Russian UT-15. However, he was confident

---

[8] Page 240

that the innovation would work just as the American had promised.

Before heading out to the aircraft boarding area, Lince stepped momentarily inside his team's tent. He tore off a page from his log book and put it in his jumpsuit pocket along with a pen and a spare Russian altimeter.

He decided to write down his sister's address in the plane and then give it to Jake later on. His next jump would be individual accuracy and none of his teammates would be on that same flight.

Captain Whittle had been right about the D-Bag. Lince's parachute deployed more gradually and softer with the bag than with the original deployment sleeve. He scored a perfect dead center landing on the pea gravel pit. While the score had nothing to do with the D-Bag, it would keep the hardliners from accusing him of having a bad jump because of an unwarranted gear modification.

Lince cleared the landing pit and double-checked that nobody was watching. He kneeled down on the grass and disassembled the deployment bag, then put the note with his sister's address inside along with the Russian altimeter he promised to Jake.

Lince suspected that Captain Whittle had created the D-Bag episode as an excuse to make contact with him. Jake had most likely mentioned to him the conversation that he and Lince had by the food tent. For an instant, he thought of writing a note to Captain Whittle and tell him that he was looking for a way to flee from Peru, but promptly decided against it. He could not see a way in which the Golden Knights' captain could help him get away from his team, or spirit him out of that country for that matter. After that day's encounter with the Americans, he knew the DSE agents would redouble their vigilance on him. The D-Bag episode had now reduced Lince's chances to escape in Peru to zero.

Nick dropped off his gear in the packing area and headed straight to the USA tent to return the D-Bag. He had folded the bag in two to keep the note and the altimeter from falling out by accident.

"Thank you, Chuck. The bag is certainly a huge improvement over the sleeve. Now I need to convince the Russians to build us a much smaller parachute pack."

"Nick, you are welcome. Let's hope Comrade Boris will oblige and change the old UT-15 design. If anything, it would look more stylish."

When the Pan-Americans came to its end, the Cuban team walked out with the silver medal in the team accuracy event, placing close behind the Golden Knights. It was the first medal ever won by Cuba at an international skydiving event. However, the victory in Peru would soon be muddled by political intrigues and accusations leading to the first mass purge ever at the Cuban skydiving club.

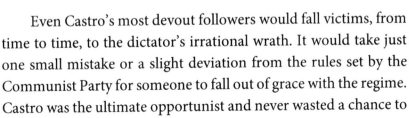

Even Castro's most devout followers would fall victims, from time to time, to the dictator's irrational wrath. It would take just one small mistake or a slight deviation from the rules set by the Communist Party for someone to fall out of grace with the regime. Castro was the ultimate opportunist and never wasted a chance to set an example and keep the fear alive. That was a fundamental part of his ghoulish political game.

Lince would be the first casualty of the selective purge that took place after the team returned from Peru. In all, it took the DSE four weeks to collect and process the information brought back by agents Yolanda and Benitez. The secret police had taken their time to make their case against Lince and other members of the delegation. Meanwhile, Tucán had made a satire of the scandal in Peru and named it *Perugate* after Richard Nixon's *Watergate* scandal.

While the *Perugate* sanctions were being deliberated behind the curtains, the regime went on to milk the team's second place victory at the Pan American Championships for propaganda purposes. The team members were featured in newspaper and magazine articles, appeared in several televised interviews and, were ultimately ordered to march with their silver medals at the official May Day parade.

Once the charade was over, the skydivers were told to surrender their medals to a glass display at the club's headquarters. As with every other accomplishment attained by Cuban athletes at international events, Fidel Castro had hijacked the skydiving team's victory in Peru.

THE LYNX

Chapter 19

Keep your face always toward the sunshine-and shadows will fall behind
you.

— *Walt Whitman*

On May 20th, 1975, Lince was summoned to Avelino Maracas'
office at Cayo la Rosa. Maracas had taken over the job as the head
of the parachute operations after Medin got himself in trouble. One
night during a competition in Cienfuegos, Medin got drunk and
shot a jumper in the neck from afar with his .45 pistol. While
the jumper hardly received a flesh wound, the unsavory
episode marked the end of Medin's career in the skydiving club.

Nobody at the drop zone had a clue where Maracas had come
from, only that he knew nothing about skydiving. The position was
given to him solely because of his credentials in the Communist
party. It was typical of the party to move its most raucous
commissars from one place to the next and keep things in check.
Aloof and arrogant, Maracas didn't make any friends during his
brief tenure at Cayo la Rosa.

As he stepped into the office, Lince noticed an eight-by-ten
black and white picture of Jake Brake and him on top of Maraca's
desk. Judging from the angle it was taken, it had to be the shot he

saw agent Yolanda snapping through the telescopic lens of her Nikon camera in Collique.

"What were you talking about with the American?" Maracas asked, holding the picture in front of Lince's face.

"We were just talking about the accident where the young woman lost her arm, nothing else."

"Only about the accident?"

"Yes, that was all."

"Why then on the next day the captain of the U.S. team asked you to test jump a parachute component that was not made for your rig. Wasn't that too much of a coincidence?"

"I didn't ask anything from the Americans. They came up with that idea on their own accord."

"You deliberately put yourself at risk of having a malfunction during the competition and getting disqualified for that jump."

"Maracas, you were in Collique on that day. You know very well that Bienvenido approved the jump with the D-Bag, and that everyone concurred there was no risk involved. The Americans had been using the same bags on their parachutes for a while, and they all had perfect deployments. Did you ever read the event rules? An equipment malfunction does not disqualify a jumper on a competition jump. In the unlikely event of that happening, I would have gotten an automatic re-jump. I've been around parachutes long enough to know the modification was going to work as it actually did. You better learn a little about skydiving in general."

"Had you said no to the Yankee from the start, Bienvenido would have never been put on the spot."

"Maracas, you people talk about peaceful coexistence all the time, but you don't practice what you preach. The American just wanted to be friendly and show us a novel system that we might find useful someday."

"Unfortunately for you, neither the State Security nor the Communist Party sees it that way. Chuck Whittle is an officer in the U.S. Army and therefore an enemy of the Cuban revolution. Besides, nobody ever authorized you to engage the Americans in any way."

With a smirk pasted on his face, Maracas went on to read a letter from the Communist Party that condemned his behavior in Peru. The letter accused Lince of having an ideological weakness, and behaving against the principles of the revolution in a foreign country. By interacting with the Americans, the skydiver had meddled in matters of foreign relations without the approval of the Cuban government.

Maracas took a long, deliberate pause before delivering the final blow. The nasty look in his eyes revealed he was the bearer of bad news.

"You have been suspended from all sports activities in Cuba indefinitely. The revolutionary government considers you unfit to represent Cuba at international events ever again. Your skydiving career is over. You must now empty your locker, return all government property given to you and leave the drop zone."

"And you can go straight to hell" Lince scolded him as he walked out of the office.

Five years after successfully infiltrating one of the most elite sports in Cuba, Lince had fallen out of grace with the regime. Not even his good friend Bienvenido could, or would even dare to help him now. Within days of Lince's demise, the regime also imposed disciplinary sanctions to four other members of the Cuban delegation to Peru, including Maracas. The charges brought against the men ranged from having relationships with Peruvian women, to accepting money and gifts from strangers.

In the following weeks, three of Lince's teammates, all of them members of the Communist Party, were called to active military duty and deployed to the war in Angola. That same week, Maracas got fired from his job as head of skydiving operations and had all his Communist Party privileges revoked. Rumors had it that the disgraced commie was sent load pesticides at a remote crop duster base on the Isle of Pines.

"Nick, I just got a memo from the administration. It says that your job was eliminated due to budget constraints," Roberto said. "But between you and me, there have been no other cuts. It had to be something else."

"I know Roberto. I kind of expected this to happen."

"You need to report to the labor department on Monday. If you don't, you'll risk being charged with vagrancy and face jail time. The new labor law states that everyone must either be enrolled in school, or gainfully employed. I'm sorry, Nick. You had been a great asset to our department."

One day after getting kicked-out of the sport, the Secret police got him fired from his job at the university. The regime was set on making an example of the dishonored member of the national skydiving team. Lince realized the DSE would try anything to break his spirit and braced himself for their move

After a long wait in line at the labor department, a sluggish woman behind a small window gave Lince more bad news.

"We have very few vacancies, comrade. Actually, I only have

two jobs to offer you today. The first one is as a crocodile hunter in the Zapata Peninsula. The other is as a farmhand at a rice research station near San Antonio. Which one would you like to sign up for"

His decision was a split second one. Lince had heard about the scores of former crocodile hunters with missing limbs living in the mosquito-infested swamps of Zapata.

"I'll take the job as a farmhand," was his decisive reply.

The woman jotted down his personal information and handed him a slip with his job assignment.

"You must show up at the rice farm of Niña Bonita first thing tomorrow morning. The pay is seventy pesos per month."

Nick arrived at the rice research station of Niña Bonita at seven-thirty the next morning. He found the research facilities nestled on the southwest edge of a ten-thoousand-feet long, eight lane highway located not far from the secret Soviet base of Lourdes. Very few people on the island had ever heard of the super secret Soviet Signals Intelligence base. And those who had knowledge of its existence did not dare to talk about it.

On the other hand, the eight lane superhighway that doubled as a military runway was known by many people in Havana. Every so often, the local newspaper would announce the highway's closure to vehicular traffic in anticipation of scheduled MIG jet fighter maneuvers.

In a VOA broadcast, the commentator had suggested that the ten thousand feet long runway between Havana and San Antonio was linked to the operations of the Soviet base at Lourdes. [9]

The news didn't come as a surprise to Lince. That was the approximate area where the Russians had deployed a Spetsnaz tank brigade in the early sixties. Rumor had it the brigade was still on the island to help Castro fend-off a foreign invasion or, to suffocate an internal uprising. The runway could also be used by the Russians to land long-range transport aircraft and evacuate the base in case of the imminent collapse of Castro's regime.

Coincidentally, it was the same highway that he and Michael Quinn had stumbled into by accident four years earlier while looking for an access to the eastern banks of the Ariguanabo River.

On his first day in the rice fields, Lince was distracted by the sound of an airplane flying overhead. He put down his hoe and shielded his eyes with the palm of his hands as he scanned the cloudless skies above. Soon enough, he spotted an AN-2 biplane circling about four miles to the west. Seconds later he saw several parachutes opening a few hundred feet below the plane. It was then that he realized the agriculture station was located a few miles east of the drop zone at Cayo la Rosa.

"The parachutists are a great amusement to us," a man standing near Lince said. "By the way, my name is Alvaro. I'm one of the engineers here."

"Nice meeting you, Alvaro. My name is Nick, but my friends call me Lince."

"You don't look like a typical laborer, Lince."

"Actually, this is my first time doing this kind of work. Up until last week, I was one of those guys amusing you under my parachute. But some smart people thought that my talents could be

[9] Page 237

put to better use pulling weeds in the rice paddies."

Alvaro chuckled. "Sorry, I didn't mean to sound rude, but that was very funny. You are not the only athlete who has been sent to work here, though. Soon enough you'll run into a very tall guy named Gainza—a former member of the national basketball team. What kind of work did you do besides skydiving?"

"I was an English translator at the University."

"That's interesting. We have tons of English books and abstracts on rice genetics that are vital to our work. But most of us can't read English and we don't have a translator. I will talk to the station manager today and ask him to put you to work as our translator. But, that's only if you agree to it."

"I wouldn't mind that at all, Alvaro. I'll be obliged. I'm sure they have my employment application on file. All my past work references are there."

The next day, Lince found a new job waiting for him. The station manager had set up an air-conditioned office with a desk, two chairs, an electric typewriter and an English-Spanish dictionary of scientific terms. On top of the desk were stacks of books and abstracts related to rice genetics. He noticed that most of them had been published by the Rice Research Institute in the Philippines.

After being introduced to some of the station engineers and technicians—the people who would help him become acquainted with rice genetics terminology—Lince started working on his new assignment. He thanked providence for placing Alvaro in his path, and for saving him from roasting in the blistering sun of the rice paddies.

When the U.S.S.R. sent a scientist to the rice station to conduct genetic research, Lince was commissioned to become his personal assistant and interpreter. Sergei Samarov spoke perfect English, but not a word of Spanish.

Part of Lince's new job was to accompany the Russian on his frequent trips to remote parts of the island. The men would walk for hours collecting seeds from wild rice plants that grew in valleys, meadows and riverbanks. Samarov would then take those seeds to the lab and work at genetically engineer high-yield rice varieties resistant to local insects and diseases.

On their trips to the countryside, Lince and Sergei were lodged in luxurious hotels and resorts reserved exclusively for tourists and foreign technicians working in Cuba. The opulence and overabundance the government hid in plain sight from the people was evidence of the systematic segregation they were subject to in their own homeland.

"Life is great in Cuba," Samarov told Lince more than once. "We don't have these luxuries in the U.S.S.R."

That year, Lince enrolled in night school to study German. It was at that school where he met Pepín Fernandez, Cuba's national spearfishing champion. The men became very good friends.

In the months that followed, Pepín took Lince free diving to depths of 40 to 50 feet and taught him the art of shooting fish underwater. The men would swim a thousand feet or so offshore from a beach near Jaimanitas, dive down to one of Pepín's favorite reefs and return home almost every time with a couple of large snappers or groupers.

Because of his extraordinary free-diving skills, Pepín was often invited to accompany Fidel Castro on spearfishing expeditions in the pristine reefs around Cuba. Pepín knew exactly where to find just about any kind of fish swimming in the ocean.

For the most part of that year, Nick stayed home reading, listening to music and working out to stay fit. He developed a routine that would help him endure the months away from skydiving, and also keep his sanity.

A friend brought him an old parachute harness that he hung from a tree branch in his backyard. After his daily two-mile run through the neighborhood, Lince would strap himself into the harness to practice the skydiving aerobatic maneuvers while suspended in midair. He pushed himself to the limits to keep-up with his freefall skills in anticipation of the day when he might be allowed to skydive again. The harness under the mango tree was his best possible alternative to achieve that goal.

The idea of using skydiving as a means to escape from Cuba was still very much alive in the back of his mind. All along, he remained optimistic and thought of his sanction only as a temporary setback. Somehow, he believed that his dreams would become true at the end of the long and painful journey.

THE LYNX

Chapter 20

Out of difficulties grow miracles.
— *Jean de la Bruyere*

Fidel and Raul Castro had banned the circulation in Cuba of nearly every book and magazine published in the free world. Nonetheless, a large number of forbidden titles found their way into the prison island. The books were usually wrapped in plain paper to conceal the cover and then passed on secretly from one reader to the next via a selective underground network. With a pervasive shortness of entertainment, reading had become one the favorite pastimes in Cuba.

One of Lince's old schoolmates worked as a diplomatic courier for the Cuban Foreign Ministry. Abel del Valle would return home from his long overseas trips with several suitcases stuffed with blue jeans, American cigarettes, chewing gum, Scotch whiskey and the latest rock music albums—items highly coveted on the island. An inveterate reader, Abel had also smuggled into Cuba dozens of books that eventually found their way into the underground network.

Abel gave Lince a copy of a book titled Papillon, the story of an innocent man sentenced to life in prison at the penal colony of Devil's Island in French Guyana. After many years of gruesome suffering, and several attempts to flee from his imprisonment, Papillon ultimately succeeded in regaining his freedom.

Papillon became a true inspiration to Lince. That amazing story helped cement his resolve to get back on the national skydiving team and ultimately bolt from the island. If Papillon had broken free from his captivity in spite of seemingly insurmountable adversities, so would he. Eleven months from the day he made his last jump in Peru, Lince thought it was time to reach out to Bienvenido and asked his old friend for a reprieve. Bienvenido agreed to meet with him on the following evening.

All the lights in the colonial-style house had been turned off, but for a small desk lamp burning inside Bienvenido's office. He found his friend seated at the desk looking much older and more tired than the last time he saw him. There was another person in the room, sunk in an armchair with his face obscured by the shadows. It took Lince a few moments to recognize Tony Angulo, the enigmatic lieutenant from the secret police.

"It's been a while, Comrade Nickolich. How are you?" Bienvenido asked.

Lince shrugged. "*Comme ci, comme ca.* It wasn't fun to slow down from one hundred and twenty miles per hour to nearly zero."

Bienvenido smiled and gestured the skydiver to take a chair next to the DSE officer.

"I understand that you would like to skydive again."

"I do, comrade. I believe I have paid enough for my past

mistakes."

"So you know, I had a long conversation with your manager at the research station. The man spoke highly of you, and of the work you've done there."

"I enjoy my job as a translator and working hand in hand with the Russian scientist. It's been a great learning experience."

"Well, I have good news for you. The powers to be have decided to lift your sanction and allow you back in the sport. But before you get back, you must deliver a public apology to your teammates for your misconduct in Peru."

Lince nodded. "I cannot argue with that, comrade."

"I need to make one thing clear to you," Angulo intervened. "Although you can skydive again, you will not be allowed to make the national team, or travel overseas. Those are our conditions for your reinstatement."

"I'll accept that, lieutenant. I'll be glad just to have the opportunity to skydive again. I can use my knowledge to help others improve their competitive skills."

Angulo's statement didn't come as a surprise to Lince. He knew the DSE would never let him off the hook that easy.

The skydiver returned to the clubhouse on the following day to deliver the promised apology to his former teammates. In his opening statement, Bienvenido told those present that Lince would be allowed to skydive again thanks to his good behavior during his one-year suspension. He also praised the skydiver's talents and added that having him back would be of great benefit to all.

When his turn to speak arrived, Lince uttered a brief apology while trying to sound regretful. His friends thanked him for keeping his speech short and, following tradition took him to celebrate at a local hangout in the nearby Hotel Colina.

In the summer of 1976, Bienvenido stepped down as director of the Cuban Air Sports club to assume a new position with the Ministry of Foreign Relations. The man had been longing for that day to arrive. The long years of intensive training in intelligence gathering, clandestine protocols, insurgency tactics and getting groomed in the art of international diplomacy had paid off. His old mentor, Manuel *Redbeard* Piñeiro had finally reeled him to the top floor of the Department Americas. Within months, Bienvenido Garcia would start undertaking intelligence missions outside Cuba posing as a bona fide career diplomat.

The man appointed as the new head of the air sports institute was Luciano, a former crop duster pilot and a Communist hard-liner. With his old friend no longer at the helm, Lince seriously doubted that he would ever be allowed back on the national team.

In late 1976, Luciano announced that Cuba would be sending a parachute team to a friendly meet in Czechoslovakia. As Lince had expected, his name did not appear on the team roster. The DSE was sticking to their decision to keep him from traveling out of the country. Three of his former teammates didn't make the team either, but for a different reason. The men were still deployed to the war in Africa.

A few days after the skydiving team left for Prague, Lince received a phone call from Nestor Aponte, the new head instructor at the parachute club.

"Lince, two Canadians just showed up at the club's door, but nobody here understand a word they say. Can you talk to them?" Aponte handed the phone to one of the visitors.

The Canadian got on the line and introduced himself as Gabriel, a skydiver from the British Columbia. He and a friend had arrived in Havana the night before on an Air Canada flight from Toronto. The men had bought along their parachute gear and were hoping to make a few jumps on the island.

"Tell them to meet us here at eight o'clock sharp tomorrow morning, and to bring along their licences and logbooks," Aponte told Lince.

The two relaxed men that Lince found seated on the club's front stairs could have jumped out of a photograph from a rock concert in Woodstock, N.Y. he had seen in the pages of Life magazine. Both men had long hair and were dressed in tee shirts, faded blue jeans and beach sandals.

Gabriel and Derek told Lince they had learned about the skydiving club in Cuba from Oreste Chemello, a Canadian who had competed against the Cubans in Hungary.

"I remember Oreste. He was jumping a red and white Para-Plane cloud parachute."

"That's our friend" Derek said.

Aponte showed-up moments later with good news.

"We are leaving for San Nicolas shortly. Tell the Canadians that their jumps will be free of charge as our guests."

Aponte asked Lince to follow him into his office and gave him a most unusual assignment.

"Lieutenant Angulo would like you to spend as much time as possible with these two guys. The DSE wants to know what they are up to."

"No problem. I'll let you know if I notice anything out of the ordinary."

Ironically, the same people who had banned him from

traveling out of the country now wanted him to spy on the Canadians. Unbestknown to Angulo, the officer had just handed him an opportunity to send a secret message to his sister in the United States.

That morning, the weather conditions in San Nicolas were far from ideal for skydiving. A low layer of clouds had moved in over the airfield and the wind was gusting at twelve to eighteen knots. Still, Gabriel, Derek and Lince decided to board the AN-2 to make a jump from ten thousand feet. The conditions worsened after the first jump, forcing the skydivers to call it a day. [10]

Back in Havana, Lince invited Gabriel and Derek for dinner at his home. His mother was delighted to have guests from Canada and prepared a roasted chicken meal with black beans and white rice. After dinner, Lince asked his guests to join him for a drink in the backyard. He could speak there freely without fear of being overheard.

"Thanks for taking us skydiving today and for the nice dinner. Your mother is an excellent cook," Gabriel said.

"It was my pleasure. Too bad the weather did not cooperate."

"Your father mentioned that you have a sister living in the United States. When did she leave Cuba?" Derek asked.

"She got out in 1967. It's been almost ten years now. Once I joined the skydiving club, it became impossible for me to speak or write to her again. If I did, I would have been kicked out of the sport for good. The regime doesn't want us to stay in touch with family and friends living outside Cuba."

"You have not been in touch with your sister all these years?"

"Only sporadically and in secret. The last time I did so was at the Pan American Games in Peru. I had an opportunity to send her

---

[10] Page 241

a message with Jake Brake, a member of the Golden Knights. But my conversation with Jake didn't go unnoticed. One of the Cuban agents spotted Jake and I together and took a picture from a distance. That piece of evidence got me in a heap of trouble upon my return to the island."

"You couldn't talk to skydivers from other countries?"

"No, not if there wasn't another member of the team with us. Then things got more complicated. On the day after I had my conversation with Jake, the captain of the Golden Knights approached me with a most unusual request. He wanted me to try a new deployment system on my UT-15 parachute."

"Did you?"

"Yes, and that was the straw that broke the camel's back. After our return from Peru I was suspended from the sport for a whole year. It was only recently that I was allowed to skydive again. However, I'm still banned from traveling overseas."

"Nick, I will be happy to mail a letter to your sister from Canada. I can hide it inside my parachute. Nobody will find it there," Derek told him.

"That would be great. I'll write her a brief note before you guys leave tonight. By the way, are you interested in learning what's really happening in this country?"

"Absolutely."

"There is a lot going on that Castro doesn't want foreign visitors like you to know. While the people on the streets won't admit to it, everyone in Cuba has become a slave of the establishment. I'm afraid that many folks here are suffering from a mass case of Stockholm syndrome—or something very similar. Their blind fanaticism makes them appear they are under some sort of hypnotic trance."

"That's an interesting observation," Gabriel said. "However, most of what we hear in Canada about Cuba is positive. Our media never cease to praise the social and health care advancements on the island and its superior education system."

"Gabriel, Castro is a wizard in making believe Cuba is a social paradise. It's nothing like that. Nothing is really free here. Cubans pay for all the handouts by working overtime and receiving meager wages for their labor. Everyone has to work for the government at set wages."

"People outside Cuba have been duped to believe that education is free here. That's another fallacy," Nick continued. "It's only free in the sense that you don't get a bill, but it will get paid for sooner or later in many other ways."

"For starters, to be accepted into college a student must have a track record of affiliation with one of the Communist organizations. After receiving a degree from a university, his or her wages will still be substandard even when compared to those in the poorest third-world countries. For example, a doctor or an engineer only brings in about three hundred pesos per month, which means they would be paying for their education for the rest of their lives. That *invisible* loan will never get paid off."

"Health care, on the other hand, is a vital tool of the regime to keep the slaves healthy and the country going. But that's just another bubble that the failed domestic economy could never sustain on its own. Health care, and just everything else here, gets paid for by the hefty subsidies received from the Soviet Union."

"Thanks for being candid with us. Nobody here has opened up to either Derek or me. Not until now."

"Most people in Cuba won't dare to talk frankly to foreign visitors in fear of retribution. Many tourists who come here happen to sympathize with the regime out of sheer ignorance, or because of some pre-conceived political idealism. The majority of the tourists only get to see the bright side of Cuba—the resorts, the beaches, the fancy restaurants and the pretty *señoritas*."

Lince paused momentarily to listen, trying to pierce through the shadows under the trees for unfamiliar sounds.

"The regime is in control of every waking moment of our lives," he continued. "They control what and how much we can eat, what we can buy, and what we should say and do. There is no freedom of expression. We cannot emigrate or visit another country at will. Even when we travel to another city in Cuba as a private citizen, we must notify the local police and let them know where we are staying, the reason for our visit and the length of our stay. The conversation we are having at this very moment is totally against the law. If the secret police ever finds out, I would be accused of treason and sent to rot in jail."

"I guess that we take our freedoms for granted in Canada. We appreciate your trust in us. It must be very difficult to live under such oppression."

"Derek, I've been trying to get out of this place since I was a teenager. After I made it on the skydiving team, I hoped to jump ship during a competition abroad. But those plans were trashed after our trip to Peru."

"Are there any chances for your travel ban to get reversed?"

"That's my only hope. Cuba might send a team to the Pan American Games in Mexico in November of next year. If a miracle happens and I'm allowed back on the team, you can bet anything that I'm not coming back. At least not alive."

"I presume the vigilance on the team in Mexico will be extreme."

"It always is. So far, the DSE agents have made an escape abroad impossible. It might help if someone outside Cuba knew that I'm the son of an American citizen and that I want to defect."

Gabriel stood silent for a few seconds. "Nick, what I'm about to tell you might seem to you like a strange coincidence. Not too long ago, I met an American skydiver who's well connected in Washington, DC circles. His name is Jock Covey and he is a personal assistant to the outgoing secretary of state Henry Kissinger. Jock is currently helping Kissinger transition back to private life."

"I've heard the name Kissinger before. Wasn't he the chief U.S. negotiator during the peace talks with Vietnam?"

"Same man. If you agree to it, I can call my friend upon my return to Canada and tell him about your dilemma. I'm sure he will be happy to pass on the information to Kissinger. Although Kissinger is on his way out of office, he should have a way to channel your appeal to the right people at the State Department."

It was a tough call. Up until that day, nobody other than his old neighbor Michael Quinn, and his immediate family knew that he intended to use skydiving as a means to escape. For the most part, he had been a loner, a solo performer in his journey to deceive the Cuban wolves. Now the Canadians also knew his secret, but Lince sensed he could trust the men implicitly. He had always pretty accurate when judging people.

On the other hand, sharing his secret with a large agency like the U.S. State Department could be a dangerous proposition. His father once told him that Castro had many sympathizers in the State Department, and was convinced that some people there had actually facilitated the rebels' victory in 1959.

Lince realized that the minute the Canadians relayed his appeal to Henry Kissinger by way of the aide, the whole thing would become a conspiracy. If the Cubans ever found out, the ensuing punishment would be unthinkable.

He thought about the Canadian's proposal for a minute or so. Acting against conventional wisdom, he gave Gabriel his consent to pass the information to his friend in D.C. He feared that if he blew that one opportunity to reach out to the Americans, he might never have another chance again. There had to be a reason why destiny had put the Canadians in his path.

"If you think you can trust your friend with this information, by all means, please tell him."

The day after Gabriel and Derek left for Canada, Lince received a phone call from Lieutenant Angulo.

"What is your take on the unusual visit by the Canadian skydivers?" The lieutenant asked him.

"Gabriel and Derek are two nice guys who love skydiving and came here to have a good time. They have very progressive ideas, and constantly praised the social advances made by our revolution. They were very impressed with the fact that we get to skydive for free."

The officer thanked Lince and then added that his cooperation with the DSE would not go unnoticed.

Three weeks later, Lince got a surprise phone call from Gabriel. The Canadian was staying at the Hotel Deauville in Havana and wanted to see him. While vacationing in Venezuela, Gabriel had decided to change his return trip to Montreal by adding an overnight stop in Cuba. The men agreed to meet in the lobby of the Deauville at seven that same evening. Gabriel must have some news for him.

After hanging up with Gabriel, Lince placed a call to Nestor Aponte to tell him of his planned meeting with the Canadian at the Deauville. Lince knew the DSE had likely intercepted the phone call and could be waiting to see his reaction. Aponte told him he did not object to the meeting and sent his best wishes to Gabriel.

Lince asked the taxi driver to drop him half a block from the Deauville. Walking the last stretch to the hotel would allow him to check for the presence of plainclothes policemen in the area. Half the way there, he indeed noticed two men standing next to a red Buick on the other side of the street. *Angulo's men.* Gabriel was already waiting for him by the hotel's front door.

"Nick, it's great to see you again. Can I buy you a beer?"

"Thank you, but it's so nice outside. Should we go for a walk on the Malecón instead?"

"That sounds like a great idea," Gabe said.

Lince wanted to talk with Gabriel somewhere where their conversation could not be overheard with the use of directional microphones. It was winter in Havana, the time of the year when the surf crashed relentlessly against the sea wall and silenced every word spoken on the sidewalk above.

The Canadian had fresh news for him. He had spoken to Jock Covey and told him about Lince's plans in Mexico. Jock promised Gabriel to deliver the information to "the right person," whom the Canadian was convinced was Secretary of State Kissinger.

Lince quivered. The thought alone that strangers in the United States already knew of his plans made him feel uneasy. But there was no turning back now. The die had been cast.

"I hope you get to travel to Mexico and things work out for you, Nick. I wish you the best of luck."

"Thanks again for everything. If all goes well, I will pay you a visit in Canada in the near future."

The phone rang at Lince's home the next morning. It was Lieutenant Angulo.

"Aponte told me that you met with one of the Canadian skydivers again. Why was he back in Cuba?"

"Apparently, Gabriel had an opportunity to reroute a trip from Venezuela to Canada via Havana at no extra cost to him He said he just wanted to say hello to us, and to see Cuba again. It's obvious that he loves our country."

"Where did you guys meet?

"It was nice outside and Gabriel said he needed some fresh air after his flight. We went for a walk along the Malecón." Lince knew that Angulo had to know the answer to that question.

Angulo thanked him for the information, but the DSE officer didn't sound very happy that time around. He was obviously frustrated that he and Gabriel didn't meet in the hotel, which made it impossible for his agents to listen to their conversation.

To keep his sanity in the months ahead, Lince realized he would have to forget the whole Gabriel—Kissinger—State Department episode and focus solely on his skydiving training. That was the only thing within his power, which could open his door to freedom. Before anyone could help him, he would have to make the national team again, and then find a way to break his restriction to travel outside Cuba.

THE LYNX

Chapter 21

You know you are truly alive when you're living among lions.
— Karen Blixen-Out of Africa.

By the end of 1975, the first Cuban mercenary troops deployed in Angola began to trickle back to the island—all but a few thousand men that were killed in combat and left buried in African soil. Lince was relieved to see Kymbe and his other teammates returning home safely.

The Cuban troops had been strictly forbidden to talk about the war in Africa, even with their own family members. However, it was next to impossible to keep a Cuban's mouth shut for too long. Of all the people who dared to share their experiences in Angola, nobody told them with more vividness and color than Kymbe. His stories were also the most exaggerated of all. The guy was funny, original and loved by everyone at the parachute club.

"Just a few weeks ago, I was dodging bullets in the snake-infested jungles of Africa," Kymbe started out one afternoon in his deep tone of voice. "Operation Carlota was then top secret and we were ordered not to tell anyone where we were being deployed to."

The skydiver had been lying in a bunk bed, wrapped in a mosquito net with multiple burnt holes in it. Kymbe had made the tiny holes with the red-hot tip of his filterless *Populares* cigarettes while trying to sear the mosquitoes that had snuck inside the net.

"I was the cameraman on a film crew embedded with a Special Forces unit that crossed into Cabinda from Congo Brazzaville in mid 1975. We got in wearing civilian clothes and pretending to be migrant oil rig workers. Once in the African enclave, the Angolan army brought us our uniforms, AK-47 rifles, ammunition and hand grenades, along with a couple of 14, 5 mm pieces—Russian four-barrel anti-aircraft guns."

"Within days of our arrival in Cabinda, our camp was attacked by a Bakongo tribe loyal to Jonas Savimbi, one of the top rebel leaders in Angola. It was then when our unit commander, for lack of better artillery decided to try the anti aircraft gun as an infantry weapon. After the dust settled, there was little left standing where the AA rounds hit and exploded. All the surrounding vegetation had vanished just like magic."

Kymbe paused to take a drag from his cigarette.

"Our armored vehicles, artillery pieces and support material arrived two weeks later aboard a Cuban cargo ship. But other than a sporadic scrimmage with the Bakongo rebels, we didn't get to see much action throughout our stay in Cabinda. Our Special Forces unit was mission specific. Ironically, we were in the enclave was to safeguard the operations of a crude oil production facility owned by Chevron—an American owned company."

"But we got a harsh payback for hitting the rebels with the AA guns. The story I'm about to tell you is not for the faint hearted and shall not be repeated outside these walls," Kymbe whispered as he scanned the area outside his mosquito net with his bulgy hazel eyes.

"Cabinda is a gloomy place where it never stops raining. One time, the downpour went on for so long that we were forced to hunker down at the camp for a solid week. Several days into the deluge, two soldiers from an overdue scout patrol found their way back to our base. The guys were in bad shape, soaked to the core, and had very bad news. A tribal guerrilla apparently loyal to the Cabinda nationalists had ambushed their recon platoon, the same guys we nearly decimated after our arrival. Outnumbered ten to one, the entire platoon surrendered. The only two guys who managed to escape the ambush had been following the patrol at the rear."

"Our men tracked the guerrilla and their prisoners all the way to a small encampment a few kilometers from the ambush site. From their hideout, they watched in dismay as their comrades got lined up single file and shot in the back of their heads. The cannibals dismembered the bodies using axes and machetes and then poured their blood into large ceramic jars. Needless to say, those were the savages we feared the most during our deployment in Africa. It was nearly impossible to sleep at night knowing there were cannibals lurking in the nearby jungle. Or black mambas and other poisonous snakes for that matter."

Without television or other means of entertainment at the drop zone, Kymbe's fantastic tales about the war in Angola soon became everyone's most anticipated pastime during the team's leisure hours. The skydiver's repertoire seemed to be inexhaustible.

In 1976, Cayo la Rosa was shut down to all skydiving and glider operations. After years of operating too close to the José Martí international airport and the San Antonio air base, the Cuban authorities decided the club's activities were an unnecessary hazard to the local air traffic. There had been a few close calls, but never an accident, though.

In one particular incident, a MIG 21 jet fighter from San Antonio had accidentally buzzed Kymbe and another jumper while they were descending under their open parachutes. The turbulence left behind by the jet turbine almost collapsed their canopies. Kymbe swore having seen the frightened look in the pilot's eyes behind the MIGS's cockpit Plexiglas.

The skydivers found a temporary home at a small airfield near the town of La Coloma in Pinar del Rio. The old team members from Peru regrouped and resumed their training, which had been put on hold for too long. After a one-year absence from the sport, however, the men were still unbeatable in all the skydiving disciplines. Kymbe and Lince were still above the rest and always competing neck and neck for first place. They were also best of friends.

While training at La Coloma, Lince witnessed his first skydiving fatality ever. That day, the parachute club lost a talented jumper and an all around great fellow.

Lince and three of his teammates had exited the AN-2 plane at ten thousand feet above ground to perform a free-fall formation jump. They were followed out the door by five more skydivers. The first group performed their rehearsed formations, released their grip at twenty-five hundred feet, and tracked away from one another. All the jumpers deployed their parachutes without incident.

However, nobody in the air noticed that one of the jumpers from the second group had disengaged himself from his open parachute and got back in free fall, or saw him disappearing below the cloud layers. Unseen by the jumpers above, Narciso Marti impacted on a thorny marabou bush at one hundred and twenty miles per hour. His reserve parachute never deployed.

The entire jump had been observed from the ground by a Russian coach with the aid of powerful TZK binoculars. Visibly shaken, Alexander Dunayev broke the news to the skydivers after they landed.

"*Niet zapasnoi*, no reserve—why?" he exclaimed, raising his arms in a hopeless gesture.

The initial assumption was that Narciso had experienced a minor malfunction not visible from the ground that had rendered his main parachute unsafe for landing. Many things could have caused the problem—a line over the canopy, a line entanglement, or perhaps a tear in one of the panels. He decided to cut-away from his main, but why did he fail to open his reserve parachute?

There were too many questions, but not one single answer—at least not yet.

Dunayev rounded up every able body in the field and organized them into four search parties. Meanwhile, the Antonov jump plane started to make low-altitude passes over the area after the pilot got word of the accident. It didn't take long for the pilot to spot a body in the marabou bushes and radio in the location of the point of impact.

Two local farmers and a team of paramedics eventually reached Narciso's body after cutting through the marabou thicket with machetes and carried him to the road. Lince noticed that both the harness and the front-mounted reserve parachute were still strapped to the body, and that Narciso's right hand was tightly gripped around the reserve release handle.

At that moment, he knew the exact cause of why Narciso failed to activate his reserve parachute. Back at the base, he asked both Kymbe and Tucán to meet him in the gear storage room. He would show them what had killed their friend—something that could have killed him as well.

A few weeks earlier, Narciso and Lince had performed a radical modification on their reserve parachutes. To the men, packing a large Russian reserve parachute canopy inside a smaller Czech reserve container had seemed like a perfect solution to gain a second or two in the style event. While the small Czech reserve canopies were out of date, the packs were still airworthy. The Russian Z1 reserves, on the other hand, were all good but much too bulky. The solution was to figure out a match. The end result, however, proved to be fatal.

In a style free-fall competition jump, a small belly-mount reserve pack made it easier for a jumper to tuck up his knees to gain speed in the performance of the acrobatic flat turns, and in doing back loops. It was all about aerodynamics. The smaller the mass, the less resistance the body offered to the wind in free fall.

In competition, one second, or even a fraction of it could make the difference in making or not the national team, or getting on the podium at an international event. To Lince, it could mean his ticket to freedom.

While it took both Narciso and Lince a considerable effort to close the parachute packs, it never crossed their mind that this would also make it difficult to pull the reserve ripcord if they were to experience a main malfunction.

Lince was convinced that after Narciso released his main parachute due to some unknown problem, he didn't open his reserve simply because he was incapable of doing so. It was evident that the pull force he encountered was beyond his physical capabilities.

With Kymbe and Tucán as his witnesses, Lince geared up to perform a ripcord pull test on his own reserve parachute.

After several hard pulls, Lince managed to dislodge the ripcord pins and get his reserve container open. He had both his feet on the ground, which offered him considerably more leverage than he would have had while in free fall. Had he experienced the same problem as Narciso did, he might not have been able to pull his reserve ripcord either.

The Civil Aeronautics Institute appointed a special commission to investigate Narciso Marti's fatal accident. To Lince's bewilderment, several officials from the parachute club testified before the panel that there was nothing wrong with Narciso's reserve parachute. One of the club instructors declared that the Russian coach had watched the reserve canopies swap and didn't see any problems with it.

Another instructor testified that Narciso have had family problems in the past, suggesting that he was suicidal. Two days later, the panel arbitrarily concluded that Narciso had deliberately chosen not to activate his reserve parachute and called his death a suicide.

Lince was angered by the conclusions. He knew Narciso had not killed himself and that the Russian coach was not at fault in any way.

On the same day the verdict was released, Lince got a phone call from Colonel Kleber Marti, Narciso's oldest brother. The colonel wanted to meet with him and discuss the commission's report on his brother's death.

That would be the second time that Lince met Kleber face-to-face. The first time had been at his brother's funeral. Over six feet tall, lanky, with a hawkish nose and ice-cold blue eyes, Kleber Marti was the head the feared Ministry of Interior in the province of Oriente. From his looks alone, Kleber coud have been mistaken for an officer from the German S.S. A perfect pick for the job.

"I'm convinced that your brother experienced some kind of problem with his main parachute, decided to cut-away from it, but was unable to pull the reserve ripcord," Lince told Kleber.

"Why wasn't he able to pull the ripcord?"

"The problem had to do with the modification we both performed on our reserve rigs. Both Narciso and I had packed a large reserve parachute in a container intended for a much smaller canopy size. The extra fabric apparently exerted too much pressure on the flap that housed the ripcord closing pins."

"Did you guys try to open the parachutes on the ground?"

"In hindsight, we should have tested the ripcord's pull before taking the reserve on an actual jump. But unfortunately we didn't. The pull force that Narciso encountered proved to be too much for his physical ability."

"Are you willing to make that same statement before a second investigation committee?"

"Of course. But I would like to back up my argument with some scientific proof. I will need access to the reserve parachutes in question, and authorization to conduct a pull test using a mechanical tension device. The equipment is currently under lock and key as forensic evidence."

"I'll make sure you get a tension measuring device. And that you are allowed to perform any test that you deem necessary."

When Kleber drove away, Lince realized he had made an improbable alliance with a very influential man in Castro's innermost circle. Only a powerful MININT officer like Kleber could override his restriction to travel out of Cuba. He had to find a way to mention the issue to the colonel the next time they met.

Kleber didn't waste time. The next day, the club ordered Peter Fandiño, one of their parachute instructors, to perform the tension gauge test. Peter was both an experienced skydiver and an excellent rigger. Along with Tucán, Kymbe and Lince, he had been part of the first four-man relative work formation ever performed in Cuba. Lince knew Peter since jump school and was convinced that his friend would not yield under pressure from the club bosses. Although he would have liked to conduct the test himself, he was confident about Peter's rigging skills and honesty.

Peter repacked Narciso's reserve parachute in its modified configuration and tested the pull force on the ripcord handle with a mechanical gauge. The results could have not been more conclusive. It took over forty-two pounds of pull force on the handle to dislodge the pins and get the parachute pack open—more than twice the fifteen-pound maximum recommended for a belly-mounted reserve parachute. As Lince had thought all along, Narciso's fate got sealed the moment he closed his reserve container.

Peter and Lince were called to testify before the newly appointed accident investigation panel. The skydivers presented the results of the ripcord pull test and offered their personal opinion on what might have caused Narciso's death. After a short deliberation, the commission reversed the original verdict. It concluded that an improperly modified reserve parachute had been the cause of the accident. Narciso's family name had been cleared for good.

That same afternoon, Kleber phoned Lince to tell him that he was in the neighborhood and wanted to see him before returning to Santiago de Cuba. The men went for a short drive in Kleber's car.

"I would like to thank you for standing your ground before the accident committee."

"It was my duty to bring up the truth, colonel."

"You have cleared my family's name and for that I'm forever grateful. Is there anything I can do for you?"

"There is indeed something you can do for me, colonel. I don't know if you are aware of this, I have been banned by the DSE from travelling out of Cuba. After our last overseas event in Peru, I was accused of making contact with members of the USA team. It was the Americans who approached me and not the other way around. In any case, those encounters were inconsequential."

"Upon our return to Cuba I was suspended from the sport for a year," Lince continued. "It's only fair that I get another chance to represent our country at international skydiving events."

"Nick, all I can do is to have your case revisited by the DSE. By the way, have you ever thought of becoming more involved in our revolutionary process? Like joining the Communist Youth?"

"Of course I have, Colonel," he lied.

The colonel remained pensive momentarily.

"In that case, there are two comrades I'd like you to meet. They are Patricio and Tony De la Guardia, the commanders of the Ministry of Interior Special Forces. Both Patricio and Tony are currently in Havana, but will be returning to Angola very soon. I will see that you get to meet them before they leave. Thanks again for your help and good luck."

Chapter 22

Fear of danger is ten thousand times more terrifying than danger itself.
— *Daniel Defoe*

The scions of a Cuban upper middle class family, Tony and Patricio de la Guardia were sent to study in the United States in the mid-fifties. While living in Florida, the twins raised funds for Castro's revolution and got involved in the shipping of weapons to the guerrillas in Cuba. After the 1959 rebel victory, Castro rewarded Tony and Patricio for their loyalty by placing them in charge of the security detail for Commander Ramiro Valdez, Cuba's new Minister of Interior.

Patricio and Tony went on to found the MININT Special Forces, an elite unit independent of the Cuban Army and outside Raul Castro's control. The Special Forces answered directly to the commander-in-chief and were regarded as Fidel's personal storm troops. Not by coincidence, the SF headquarters was located less than one mile from *Punto Cero*—point zero, Castro's highly guarded compound in the neighborhood of Siboney.

After Castro's visit to Chile in 1971, the Cuban dictator

ordered Patricio to provide training to President Salvador Allende's personal security detail. Reportedly, the Cuban general was inside the presidential palace of La Moneda on the day General Pinochet stormed the building in a bloody coup d'état, and where the estranged socialist president presumably committed suicide. Patricio and a few other Cubans escape the firefight and sought refuge at the Cuban Embassy in Santiago de Chile.

At the start of the Africa campaign, Castro dispatched Patricio as a high-level military advisor to Marxist president Agostinho Neto. In Angola, both Patricio and Tony participated in countless military operations against UNITA, the FNLA and the regular South African army. While in Africa, Tony and Patricio were believed to have smuggled millions of dollars in ivory and diamonds into Angola from Mozambique. The booty was allegedly flown to Havana on military flights and stored at the Ministry of Interior vaults.

Tony de la Guardia was known to most as a daring free spirit. Every so often, he would be spotted in the streets of Miami and New York, where he met with members of Castro's intelligence network in the United States. Since the early days of the Cuban revolution, Castro had systematically planted dozens of spies in the United States with the mission to infiltrate every Cuban organization in exile, and also top-secret U.S. agencies including the CIA and the Defense Intelligence Agency.

Operating on an unlimited budget, Tony and Patricio traveled the world with impunity and were once considered the most dangerous and valuable secret assets of the Cuban government. Some people in the MININT viewed Tony de la Guardia as an intrepid adventurer, and a few of his colleagues even called him the *James Bond* of the Caribbean.

Becoming part of Patricio and Tony de la Guardia's special

operations group was not exactly what Lince had in mind. Although he was at the age when most men are easily allured by adventure and the intrigue of covert operations, entering into that murky world would have made his goal of escaping to freedom far more problematic. It was one thing to flee from a sports team at an international competition. It would be a much different story to defect from the Ministry of Interior Special Forces. That kind of engagement would be way too dangerous and could complicate his life in the long run. He also realized that a thorough background check by the MININT could uncover his earlier medical release from the army. What would happen then?

Kleber drove a hard bargain though. The Cuban intelligence colonel had made it practically impossible for Lince to refuse to meet with Patricio and Tony de la Guardia and avoid the consequences that such encounter could set off. Kleber was a smart and dangerous man to whom Castro had entrusted the security of the province of Oriente, the most strategic region on the entire island.

While the Colonel intended to make good on his implicit promise to have Lince's travel restrictions lifted, he would make sure he didn't get burnt in the process.

Lince, on the other hand, had nothing to lose.

The gate sentry at the Special Forces Command Center checked Lince's ID card against a list of names and asked him to wait. Moments later, another officer led him through the gate and into a spacious office that had once been the living room of a modern and comfortable home.

Lince found General Patricio de la Guardia seated behind a desk at the far end of the room. His twin brother, Colonel Tony de la Guardia was at another desk to his left. Both men wore olive-drab fatigues and were armed with 9mm Makarov pistols in belt holsters. At first sight, the twins looked identical—medium height, receding hairlines and short-clipped hair. They looked like they had not slept in days.

Tony and Patricio got up at the same time to shake hands with Lince. Patricio gestured him to take a seat on a small couch across his desk.

"Kleber spoke highly of you. He said you might be interested in joining the Special Forces."

"Yes, I am."

"How is your English?" Patricio asked him in perfect English.

"Fair. I can read and write better than I can speak it."

"It sounds good to me. I've heard you are a member of the national parachute team," the man continued in English.

"Yes. I have been on the team since 1974."

"Are currently you training for any competitions?"

"Cuba has been invited to compete at the Pan American Games in Mexico next November. I hope to make it on that team."

"Then we should wait until you get back from that event before bringing you on board. We don't want you to get distracted from your training."

"I appreciate your consideration, colonel."

"By the time you get back, we might already have approval from the Ministry of Interior for you to join," Patricio told him.

"The application is a long process that can take several months. However, we can get the ball rolling if you fill out the papers today. Good luck to you in Mexico".

That was the first and last time Lince would meet with Tony and Patricio de la Guardia. A sergeant ushered him to a room next door where he filled out the application for the MININT Special Forces, a unit he hoped he would never have to join.

Many years later, Lince learned that Tony and Patricio de la Guardia had become the victims of their own crimes. In a desperate move to inject dollars into Cuba's cash-strapped economy, Castro rolled the dice and decided to undertake a daring and risky operation. He wanted a piece of the lucrative international illicit-narcotics business, all while helping destroy the American imperialistic society from the inside.

Patricio and Tony were the perfect men for such mission. Castro ordered the twins to arrange for a secret meeting with the bosses of the Colombian drug cartels and negotiate the transshipment of drugs from South America to the United States using Cuba as a transfer point.

The twins reached out to their connections inside the FARC, a guerrilla organization that controlled much of the cocaine production in Colombia. Subsequently, the FARC arranged for a meeting with Pablo Escobar, the kingpin of the Medellin drug Cartel. A deal was struck. Within months, airplanes loaded with cocaine started flying from airfields in Colombia to military airports in Cuba. The cocaine was then transferred to coast guard docks in Varadero and other Cuban ports and smuggled into Florida using high-speed boats, mostly *Cigarettes*. The profits for Cuba were very lucrative and the operation seemed that it could go undetected forever. Unfortunately for Castro, the Colombian business deal blew apart faster than he could have ever anticipated.

In 1989, the U.S. Drug Enforcement Administration

uncovered Castro's drug operation and exposed it to the media.

When caught red-handed by the DEA, the Cuban dictator rushed to use the twin brothers and other high-ranking Cuban military officers as scapegoats. On June 16, 1989, Cuba admitted that some high-level officers from the regime had indeed been involved in shipping Colombian drugs to the United States.

Within days of the blowup, the secret police arrested Army General Arnaldo Ochoa, Patricio and Tony de la Guardia, and other ranking officials from the MININT. Visibly drugged and sleep-deprived during a televised court martial, the defendants admitted to have participated in the drug operations with the Colombian cartel, but on their own accord and without authorization from Fidel Castro.

One of the defendants, however, broke down during the trial and stammered that the drug dealings with the Colombian drug cartel "must have been known of at the highest levels of the Cuban government."

That statement didn't come as a surprise to anyone on the island, or outside Cuba for that matter. It would have been impossible for Ochoa and the de La Guardia twins to engage in such a large-scale operation without the knowledge and blessing of the top hierarchy in the Cuban government.

During the trial, Fidel Castro paid a visit the defendants at Villa Maristas detention center. Fidel went through the trouble to remind the men that they could save their lives if they stuck to their story and kept his name out of the equation.

At the end of the court martial charade, the military tribunal sentenced General Arnaldo Ochoa, Tony de la Guardia and two other MININT officers to death by the firing squad for the supposed embarrassment they had caused Castro and the Cuban government.

For some unexplained reason, Fidel decided to spare Patricio de la Guardia's life, but still ordered the court to sentence the former general to serve thirty years in prison.

Once again, Fidel had forsaken the men who had helped him stay in power and fulfill his personal ambitions. With the execution of General Arnaldo Ochoa, Colonel Tony de la Guardia and others the Castro brothers sent yet the strongest message ever to every man and woman on the island:

In the face of grave peril, we will only look out for our own interests. Make no mistake. We are the revolution.

THE LYNX

Chapter 23

On March 15, 1977, President Jimmy Carter issued a directive to normalize relations with the regime of Fidel Castro. The directive was addressed to the Vice President of the United States, the Secretary of State, the Secretary of Defense, the Attorney General, the Secretary of Treasury, the Secretary of Commerce, the United States representative to the United Nations and the director of the Central Intelligence Agency.

In his memo, Jimmy Carter cited having conferred with the policy review committee prior to making his decision. His goal was to set in motion a legal process that would lead to the reestablishment of full diplomatic ties between the two countries. Carter stressed that the Cuban initiative would advance the interests of the United States by addressing the human rights issues on the island, curtail Castro's intervention in foreign countries, seek compensation for all American property expropriated after 1959, combat global terrorism, and ultimately hamper the Soviet Union's political and military influence in Cuba.

A team of U.S. officials was appointed to start exploratory talks with the Cuban regime. However, a number of people in and out of the island questioned the soundness of Carter's decision. It was no secret to the CIA, or to the State Department, that the Cuban regime continued to be an active promoter, financier, trainer and supporter of terrorist groups in South and Central America.

Most recently, Cuba had become deeply involved in the war in Angola and Mozambique under orders from the Soviet Union. Within months, the Cuban army deployed twenty-five thousand troops in the African continent. And most significantly, Castro had no intentions to stop his Soviet-style policy of internal repression, or the systematic violation of human rights on the island.

In spite of the overwhelming evidence that Castro violated international laws and abused the Cuban people, Carter did not back off from his decision to open up to the Cuban dictator. On September 1977, after several months of secret negotiations between the two countries, the United States and Cuba agreed to open reciprocal special interest missions in Washington, D.C. and Havana. In principle, the move would lay the foundation to normalize full diplomatic relations between the two countries.

Carter's appointee to Havana was Lyle Lane, a career diplomat who had previously served as U.S. ambassador to Uruguay and Paraguay. Castro, in turn, dispatched Ramón Sanchez Parodi, a ranking officer in the DGI—the Directorate of General Intelligence—to lead a team of seasoned spies, instigators and saboteurs in Washington, DC. For all intent and purposes, the Cuban intelligence apparatus was given carte blanche to operate with diplomatic immunity in the heart of the empire.

That sudden turn of events worried Lince. He prayed again that the information he had sent to the Americans would not fall in the wrong hands, or get whispered to a Cuban diplomat during a casual encounter between the former adversaries. Much too often, people's tongues had become dangerously loose under the influence of a few whiskeys, Rum and Cokes, or ice-cold *Mojitos*.

Part II

GENESIS

Chapter 24

History never looks like history when you are living through it.
— *John W. Gardner*

Old immigration records listed a Polish immigrant named Abraham Simjovitch as having arrived in Cuba in the early 1920s. Simjovitch, who had been forced out of his native Poland after joining the Communist League, was subsequently recruited by the Soviets as an agent for the CHEKA, the predecessor of the KGB. By way of the COMINTERN—the Communist International—the Soviets dispatched Simjovitch to Cuba with the mission to create a Marxist organization on the island. Not long after arriving in Havana, Simjovitch changed his name to Fabio Grobart, teamed-up with Julio Antonio Mella and other Cuban agitators and founded the first Cuban Communist Party.

In the 1940s, Fabio Grobart became a close advisor to Fidel Castro in matters of Marxism. Castro, already a radicalized law student at the University of Havana, was ready to listen to Grobart and embrace the communist philosophy without reservations.

Almost a decade later, in the spring of 1948, the COMINTERN ordered Castro and a few other agitators to Colombia with the mission to disrupt the inter-American student conference that was taking place in that country. It was during that conference that a popular presidential candidate named Jorge Eliécer Gaitán was killed by an assassin's bullet. Gaitan's gang-style execution triggered three days of intense rioting, which caused the death of thousands of people and nearly destroyed the city of Bogota. The incident would be later known as *el Bogotazo*.

During the days of intense violence that followed, Fidel Castro and his cohorts took to the streets inciting the people to overthrow the government of Colombia while distributing Soviet propaganda. Castro was chased down by the Colombian police and ultimately forced to seek asylum in the Cuban Embassy in Bogota.

Between 1926 and 1948, Grobart was expelled from Cuba in four different occasions, but always managed to return to the island using false documentation. Soon after Batista fled into exile to Madeira in 1959, Fabio Grobart returned to Cuba with one final mission—to participate in the signing and delivery of the island to the U.S.S.R.

Years later, Grobart was publicly recognized for his role in converting Fidel Castro into a devoted Marxist. Abraham Simjovitch, alias Fabio Grobart, was ultimately rewarded for his work with a seat of honor in the Central Committee of the Cuban Communist Party.

Another individual who played a key role in paving the way for the Soviet intervention in Cuba was Nikolai Leonov, a senior KGB agent and a close friend of Raul Castro. Raul's secret dealings with Leonov and the KGB could be traced back to February of 1953, the time when Fidel's younger brother traveled to Austria to attend a socialist youth festival.

Leonov purportedly approached Raul on the streets of Vienna, after which the men became inseparable travel companions. From Austria, Raul and Leonov traveled to

Romania, Hungary, and Czechoslovakia. At the end of their European tour, Raul and Leonov booked a return trip to Mexico aboard the Italian ship Andrea Gritti. Allegedly, it was during that Atlantic crossing that the two men began to conspire to oust Batista by way of organized guerrilla warfare. Raul, still inexperienced in matters of armed insurrections, welcomed with open arms the valuable guidance from his new friend from the KGB.

The message sent by the Kremlin to the Castro brothers was loud and clear. If the guerrilla movement succeeded in toppling Batista and establishing a Marxist regime in Cuba, the Soviet Union would provide them with unconditional military and financial support. Until then, Leonov would need to keep a low profile in his liaison role between the Kremlin and the Cuban rebels. The less the American government knew about Castro's ties with the Soviet Union, the better their chances were to topple Batista. In the end, the conspiracy worked flawlessly.

During the months that preceded Castro's infiltration in Cuba, Leonov spent many hours in Mexico lecturing Fidel, Raul and Ché Guevara in matters of Soviet politics. Meanwhile, nearly one hundred of Castro's followers were receiving military training at a remote ranch near Chalcos—a mountainous area that closely resembled the Cuban Sierras in the province of Oriente. Their military instructor was Alberto Bayo, a primeval communist who had been defeated by General Francisco Franco in the Spanish Civil War.

A second military specialist was brought to Mexico to assist Bayo in the training of the guerrillas. His name was Miguel Sanchez AKA *el Koreano*—a Cuban-born American citizen who had served in the Korean War. While Bayo remained loyal to Castro, Miguel Sanchez opted to disappear shortly before the guerrillas took sail to Cuba.

Sanchez had grown weary of both Castro and Ché Guevara. He believed that both men were extremely dangerous and would never allow him to walk out on them. He didn't think that either Ché or Fidel would be good for the future of his homeland.

The eighty-two men in the rebel expedition set to overthrow the regime of Fulgencio Batista made the trip from Veracruz, Mexico, to Cuba in November of 1956 on board a battered sixty-foot yacht. Seven days later, the group disembarked at a beach on the shores of the eastern province of Oriente, had a brief scrimmage with General Batista's forces, and then regrouped in the nearby Sierra Maestra Mountains.

From his office at the Soviet Embassy in Mexico, Leonov maintained regular radio contact with Fidel and Raul's headquarters in the Sierra Maestra and provided valuable intelligence on the movements and capabilities of Batista's forces. The intelligence was obtained regularly by KGB agents working in Cuba and then delivered to Leonov's office in Mexico. After the rebel victory in 1959, the Kremlin rewarded Nikolai Leonov for his work by appointing him as head of the KGB station in Havana.

Right from the start of his insurgent war against Batista, Fidel Castro didn't make it a secret that he would use any means available to achieve what he called "the inevitable victory of his revolution." By the late fifties, both the people of Cuba, and the officials at the U.S. State Department knew that Castro's overall strategy included the use of terrorism against civilian targets.

Castro's two main urban guerrilla factions, the 26th of July Movement and the Revolutionary Directorate, had long been engaged in a systematic campaign of terror throughout the island. A preferred method of creating havoc was by planting explosives and home-made firebombs under parked automobiles and in nightclubs, stores and movie theatres. Those well documented acts of terrorism caused both death and serious injuries to many unsuspecting bystanders over the years.

Batista's response to Castro's attacks on the civilian population was swift and bloody. The wave of arrests, torture, and street executions that followed branded his regime as one of the bloodiest ever in the history of the republic. Whether it was by guerrilla warfare, urban terrorism or police brutality, thousands of Cuban lives were sadly wasted during the years of the rebel war.

Shortly after Castro's guerrilla landed on the shores of Oriente, Batista issued a press report stating that the rebel leader had been killed in combat. But on February 1957, the New York Times learned otherwise. Fidel Castro was alive, in good health and waging a war in the mountains of the Sierra Maestra.

The Times instructed Ruby Phillips, their bureau chief in Havana, to arrange the safe passage of a journalist to the Sierras and secure the first interview ever with the rebel leader. The man chosen for the assignment was Herbert Matthews, a seasoned war correspondent who had covered both the Spanish Civil War and the Italian occupation of Ethiopia.

Castro was eager to speak to the Times' reporter. He understood that an interview printed in the widely circulated newspaper was a great opportunity to gain international support for his cause. Castro ultimately proved to be accurate in his predictions.

In a series of articles published from February 24th to 26th of 1957, the New York Times gave Batista a series of crushing blows that helped fuel the insurgent war in the mountains of Cuba. When Matthews met with Castro, the rebel leader had but a small number of poorly armed men at his command, no logistics to speak of and very little money to finance his war. But Fidel had a privileged brain and knew how to use it. On the day Mathews arrived at the guerrilla's lair, Fidel went on to parade the same men in single file over and over, duping the journalist into believing that the guerrilla force was much larger in numbers than it actually was.

Matthews's articles gave the American readers and many people from all over the world a skewed image of the rebel leader and of the purpose of his campaign.

Captivated by Fidel's charisma, the NYT reporter depicted Castro as a superb commander of a well-organized guerrilla who was scoring significant victories against the Cuban army.

After the articles appeared in the New York Times, the world started to view Castro as a tropical Robin Hood seeking equality and justice for all Cubans. Most Americans got the impression that the bearded rebel's struggle to oust Fulgencio Batista, a former army sergeant who had blown the island's electoral process, was a legitimate and noble cause.

However, not a word was mentioned ever about Castro having embraced communist ideals in his past. While Castro's Marxist tendencies had been known by the U.S. State Department since the bloody Bogota episode in 1948, that piece of information never reached the American people.

For three consecutive days, the front page of the New York Times displayed a picture of a young man with an incipient beard and holding a telescopic-sight rifle. Both the picture and the articles proved to be galvanizing.

Matthews wrote about Castro and his guerrillas with great eloquence and passion and most readers bought the story blindly. Akin to Stalin's apologist Walter Duranty, the Times' journalist used his typewritter to spread a fallacy based on his skewed outlook on reality.

Later on, Ernesto Ché Guevara would make the following statement on Matthews's interview—"The presence of a foreign journalist, preferably an American" Guevara said, "was more important for us than a military victory."

On July 1959, Herbert Matthews was quoted saying, "This is not a Communist revolution in any sense of the term. Fidel Castro is not a Communist—he is decidedly anti-Communist."

Matthews would later be known as "the man who invented Fidel."

On November 1, 1958, five members of Castro's 26th of July Movement hijacked a Cubana Airlines Viscount with twenty persons on board en route from Miami to the Cuban beach resort of Varadero. [11] The hijackers ordered the pilot to fly the plane to a landing strip inside the rebel-occupied territory of Mayari Arriba, an area controlled by Raul Castro's forces. The ill-fated flight never made it to its diverted destination. That night, the hijacked Viscount 818 turboprop plane ran out of gas and crashed into the bay of Nipe on the northern coast of Oriente.

---

[11] Page 241

Wayne Smith, then the U.S. vice-consul in Cuba, traveled to the crash site where he received a first hand account of what transpired from one of the crash survivors. Shortly after the plane took off from Miami, two of the hijackers got up from their seats and opened a door on the floor of the airplane, while two others stepped into the cockpit to subdue the pilots. The men in the cabin proceeded to retrieve machine guns, ammunition, helmets and other items that had been hidden inside a cargo hold.

The hijackers changed into dark-green uniforms and boots and strapped on armbands from the 26th of July Movement. One of the rebels told the passengers they were on the way to deliver an important package, after which the plane would be refueled and allowed to fly to Varadero. But things did not go as planned. Having run out of fuel, the pilot attempted to land the plane at an alternate airport. That's where the Viscount skidded off the runway and crashed into the bay.

In an official memo sent by Ambassador Earl Smith to Terrence Leonhardy, the chief of the Cuban desk of the State Department, Smith wrote that the Cubana Airlines Flight 495 had enough fuel to fly until 8:45 p.m. The watch recovered from the pilot's body stopped at 9:13, thus confirming that the airplane had indeed ran on empty before the crash. Seventeen people on board the airplane died that night, including the crew members and two of the hijackers. The bodies of two of the air pirates were never recovered.

The State Department believed that two of the hijackers survived the crash and swam ashore and eventually joined Castro's forces in the mountains. One of the men was identified as Edmundo Ponce de Leon, the presumed mastermind of the hijacking.

Castro rushed to deny that members of the 26th of July

movement were responsible for the action, but vice-consul Wayne Smith knew differently. Smith had been on site in the Bay of Nipe during the recovery efforts.

The vice-consul confirmed that two of the bodies pulled out of the wreckage had black and red armbands reading 26th of July still strapped on them. The hijacking of Flight 495 became the first recorded act of air piracy in U.S. aviation history.

THE LYNX

Chapter 25

Let us never forget that terrorism at its heart, at its evil heart, is a psychological war.

— *Norm Coleman*

On June 28, 1958, a group of masked guerrillas armed with M1 rifles and Thompson machine guns stormed a mining complex in eastern Cuba. In a commando-style operation, the rebels kidnapped nineteen Americans and one Canadian citizen and forced them at gunpoint to the nearby mountains. The hostages worked as engineers and technicians at the Moa Bay Mining Company.

On the following day, another group of rebels ambushed a bus carrying twenty-nine unarmed U.S. Marines and Navy personnel returning to base from a day of liberty in Guantanamo. The U.S. servicemen were ordered to get off their bus and were spirited at gunpoint into the mountains. The man who claimed responsibility for the mass kidnappings was Raul Castro, the commander of the rebel forces in the Sierra del Cristal and Fidel's younger brother.

Shortly after the abductions in Moa, Nick's father received a phone call from Mary Elmore, the wife of his good friend and business partner Raymond Elmore. Mary was eight months pregnant and had just moved back to her hometown in Louisiana to give birth to her second child. The phone line was marred with static, forcing the woman to repeat herself often.

Raymond's housemaid had called Mary on the morning of June 29 and told her that her husband never made it home the night before. The maid was worried because of rumors that a large-scale guerrilla operation had taken place in the vicinity of the mines. The next day, Mary got a call from the State Department confirming that her husband was one of the men abducted by the armed guerrillas during the flash raid.

"Victor, we've got to do everything we can to get Raymond out of there safely," beseeched the woman. "If it's money what they want, I'll give it to them. We have over ten thousand dollars in an account at the Foreign Commerce Bank in Havana."

"Mary, don't worry. I will fly to Santiago in a day or two. There is someone I know well who could send a ransom offer to Raul Castro. I'll be happy to front you the cash."

The engineer spotted Earl Smith's six-feet, six-inch frame the moment he walked out of the elevator at the American Embassy's top floor. When he called Smith on the phone that morning to learn about the kidnappings, the ambassador invited him to attend a press briefing at the embassy. The men had been good friends since President Dwight Eisenhower appointed Smith as U.S. ambassador to Cuba in 1957.

"Gentlemen, thank you for attending today's briefing," Smith began saying. "I'll get straight the point about the kidnappings at the Moa mining facilities in Oriente, and of the U.S. Marines on leave from the U.S. naval base in Guantanamo. The man claiming responsibility for the kidnappings is Raul Castro, Fidel's younger brother. This doesn't come as a surprise to our embassy. Kidnappings and other acts of terrorism have been the standard *modus operandi* of the guerrillas under the command of Fidel Castro."

"Everyone in this room remembers the recent abduction of race car driver Juan Manuel Fangio during the last Havana Grand Prix, and of the bombings of nightclubs, theaters, and other public places that have shocked Havana and other cities in recent months," Smith continued.

"Does Eisenhower have a plan to send the Marines to rescue the hostages?" A reporter seated next to Smith interrupted.

"We believe the State Department will maintain a position of neutrality with respect to Fidel Castro and his guerrillas at this point. They fear that a military action from the United States will provoke Raul to harm or kill the hostages."

"What is the solution then?" the same man asked.

"The American consul in Santiago has been instructed to negotiate the release of the hostages with Raul Castro. Meanwhile, the embassy has advised all American citizens living in that area to evacuate without delay to Santiago and other large cities in Oriente. I should have more information in the next few days. Have a good day."

Victor Daniels switched off the Beechcraft Bonanza's autopilot and began his descent over the gleaming peaks of the Sierra Maestra range. The divergent panorama before his eyes was astounding. From six thousand feet above sea level, the southern shores of Santiago appeared to him like a jagged white line painted by the restless breaking swells.

Less than a mile out, the color of the sea turned abruptly to a hue of deep blue that stretched forever into the distance. It was the point where the continental shelf met the Cayman Trench, the legendary chasm that plummeted more than twenty-five thousand feet to the bottom of the ocean. Since the days of the Spanish colonization, the deep trench has become the resting place of many ships that failed to reach the safety of the bay of Santiago.

The engineer tuned in the VHF radio to the Santiago tower frequency and requested permission to land. The air traffic controller answered almost immediately.

"Beech 498, you are cleared for landing on runway 09," said the voice over the cockpit speaker.

Victor Daniels flew the V-Tail Bonanza a good quarter of a mile out over the ocean before making a left turn and line up on a parallel course to the runway's normal approach. His plan was to stay clear of land until he had reached the entrance to the bay of Santiago, and then come in for steep approach to the runway. By staying over the water as long as possible, he hoped to minimize the chances of being hit by ground fire. The rebels believed that Batista's army was using private airplanes to conduct rekon sorties over the mountains and had threatened to shoot them out of the sky.

After a brief sighting of the Morro Castle to his right, Victor Daniels brought the airplane to a soft landing on the sizzling asphalt with a faint squeal of the tires. His mission to obtain the release of Raymond Elmore was finally underway.

"The tie-down fee is five pesos per day. Another five pesos for the night guard will make sure that nobody will get near your plane," the ramp attendant told him.

The man helped him take his luggage out of the airplane and then scribbled some numbers on a yellow tag. Victor Daniels handed the man a twenty-peso bill, the equivalent of twenty U.S. dollars.

"Please have a mechanic top off the tanks and check the air pressure on the tires. I will be heading back to Havana in the next day or two."

"I'll take care of everything myself, sir. You can pay the airport manager for the gas, and for any additional nights before you leave. Have a safe stay in Santiago."

Victor Daniels bought a pack of Chiclets at a stand in the terminal building and walked out the front door. He often recurred to chewing gum to curb a lingering craving for tobacco. Once a chain smoker, he had not touched a cigarette in almost ten years.

The engineer used his hand to shield his eyes from the blistering sun and search for his ride. It didn't take him long to spot a shiny black Chrysler New Yorker pull out of a line of parked cars and head his way.

"How about the VIP service?" a tall man asked as he stepped out of the vehicle and walked around to greet him. Lloyd Symington was a good friend from the days Victor Daniel's had lived and worked in Oriente.

"Nice to see you again, old man. I got here just in time to watch your approach from the road to the airport. Did you have a good flight?"

"It was great, thanks. I cannot think of a better way to get here. The Bonanza cruises nicely at one hundred and fifty knots, and the autopilot makes the flight practically effortless."

"How long did it take you?"

"About four and half hours, including a stop in Camaguey to refuel and grab a bite to eat. By the way, I love your car."

"It's a beauty, isn't it? We ferried it in from Miami six months ago," Lloyd said as he steered the coupe through the vehicles parked outside the airport.

"Unfortunately, things are changing much too fast around here and we no longer feel safe. Aida and I have decided to put the house on the market and move back to the States soon. By the way, there are fresh bed sheets waiting for you at our guesthouse."

"Thanks, Lloyd, but I would have to decline this time around. I'll be meeting someone for dinner tonight at the Casa Granda and already booked a room there. But we should all get together for lunch tomorrow if you can make some time."

"Aida will be delighted to see you. Any news from La Habana?"

"Not much other than the recent kidnappings. When the news about what happened in Moa reached the capital, everyone wondered why so many Americans were still living and working that close to the war zone. It's all over the news that there was an advance warning that the kidnappings could happen at any moment."

"Vic, I can assure you there was no forewarning whatsoever. Raul issued a military order to kidnap all Americans in the area under his control, but it was not released until the same day the hostages were taken. It was just a sham aimed at to legitimizing the raids. This unexpected action has forced Batista to halt all aerial bombing of the rebel-controlled area. The rebels got exactly what they bargained for. How long you think before Ike sends the cavalry?"

"It's not going to happen, Lloyd, at least that's what I heard from Ambassador Smith yesterday. Eisenhower would love to send the Marines to clear mountains from the rebels once and for all, but he faces some serious hurdles in Washington. The guy holding the ropes over there is Roy Rubottom, the assistant Secretary of State. Rubbotom has warned the White House that an armed rescue operation would give Raul Castro an excuse to kill the hostages."

After some skillful driving through Santiago's narrow streets, Lloyd brought the Chrysler coupe to a halt next to the Casa Granda. The colonial hotel was located on Cespedes Square, catty-corner to Santiago's cathedral.

"Thanks for the ride, Lloyd. I'll give you a call tomorrow morning. Please give my love to Aida."

The Casa Granda's bellhop grabbed Victor Daniels' suitcase from the car and led his guest up the stairs to the portico. In the lobby, the engineer was met by the recorded voice of Nat King Cole playing softly in the background. The familiar melody transported him to a different moment in time and soothed his senses. In spite of the ravaging war being waged on the other side of the Sierras, life in Santiago seemed endlessly unaltered.

In his late fifties and in great physical shape, Victor Daniels had a remarkable likeness to U.S. President Harry Truman. Both men were of the same stature, had the same hook nose, same resolute jaw and bright piercing eyes behind gold-rimmed glasses. Whenever the engineer walked the streets of Havana or Miami, people would invariably turn around for a second look at the man in the Panama hat who looked so much like the thirty-third president of the United States.

For several years, Victor Daniels had commuted once a month to the mines of Charco Redondo, either on a Cubana Airlines flight, or at the controls of his single-engine aircraft. When travelling on his own airplane, he left it parked at the Bayamo airport and then drove his jeep Willys some thirty kilometers to the remote mining town nestled in the northern foothills of the Sierra Maestra range.

His last trip to the mines was in the spring of 1958. The Cuban air force had augmented its systematic aerial bombing sorties of the rebel positions and it was impossible to predict where the bombs would fall, or at which bend of the road an ambush might be waiting. One day after listening to a not so distant firefight that lasted for hours, Victor Daniels decided it was time to pack his bags and go back home.

"Welcome back to Casa Granda, *Señor* Nickolich."

"*Gracias*, Martin. There is no finer hotel in all of Santiago. It's great to be back." Victor Daniels pulled a Parker fountain pen from his jacket pocket and filled out the hotel registration form.

"I'll see that your luggage is taken to your room at once. I hope you will enjoy your stay with us."

Victor Daniels handed the registration card to Martin and walked over to the restaurant to reserve a table for two with the maître d'. He then stepped into the hotel's phone booth, unhooked the handset and gave the operator a local number.

The engineer had never heard of Robert Wiecha, the second chief of U.S. consular operations in Santiago. However, Smith had given him some insights about the man. The title was just a cover. Wiecha was the CIA station chief in Santiago de Cuba and not an easy person to deal with. The call was answered after two rings.

"Mr. Wiecha, I was given your number by Ambassador Smith yesterday. I'm calling on behalf of Raymond Elmore's wife. Mrs. Elmore would like to know if there have been any demands for ransom. His family is willing to pay a reasonable sum of money in exchange for his immediate release."

"We have not heard of any money demands," Wiecha told him. "As far as we know, the reason for the kidnappings is strictly political. I urge you to abstain from making any contact with the rebels at this point. The U.S. consular office in Santiago is now handling the situation under instructions from the State Department. Any interference outside the official channels could jeopardize our negotiations and further endanger the lives of the hostages."

"I totally understand, Mr. Wiecha. Can you please call me if there is anything new in the rebels' demands? You can reach me at the Casa Granda."

Victor Daniels pulled down on the phone's metal hook to end the call. He released the hook again and gave the hotel operator a different number in the city. After a brief conversation with an old friend, he walked to the bar and ordered an ice-cold Hatuey beer, which he took with him to his room upstairs.

His suite was the same he occupied during his last stay in the hotel a few months earlier. He loved the tall windows that offered a magnificent view of Cespedes Square, the Bay of Santiago and the Sierra Maestra in the far distance. He finished his beer, folded a bed pillow double and lay down on the mattress with his clothes and shoes still on. The long flight and the beer had made his eyelids heavy. He still had another hour and half before his meeting downstairs.

Victor Daniels woke up after a short nap, took a quick shower and got dressed in a Guayabera shirt and slacks. He grabbed his .32 Cal automatic pistol from his suitcase and shoved it deep under the mattress, along with the bag with the money he intended to offer as a payment for Raymond's release.

Before taking off from a private airstrip near the town of Santa Fé, he had made a stop at the local Royal Bank of Canada branch to withdraw ten thousand U.S. dollars in cash from his personal checking account.

With some time to spare, he opened the double-fold window blinds and made himself comfortable in a wicker armchair. He sat there for a good half hour enjoying the views of the southern slopes of the Sierra Maestra—its emerald peaks glimmering under the late afternoon sun.

Somewhere in those mountains was the mining town of Charco Redondo, a remote outpost caught in the line of fire between Batista's army and Castro's rebels. The mines had been Victor Daniels' second home for the past three years of his life. In hindsight, he regretted having spent more time in Oriente than at home with his family.

Victor Daniels wondered if the local army detachment that was once under his command was still deployed in Charco Redondo, or if the rebels had already captured the town and blown open the large Mosler safe inside the administration office. There was enough dynamite in the mine's depot to do so and much more. He was one of two men who knew the combination to the safe—the other was Francisco Cajigas, one of the mine's two owners. But even if the rebels had blown the safe open, they would have found nothing of value inside.

On his last trip to Charco Redondo, Victor had taken the precaution to empty the safe. He took back to Havana all the financial ledgers, production logs, and one extremely valuable mining survey he had conducted while searching for new manganese deposits in the region.

The survey samples had revealed the presence of large pylorusite deposits a few miles from the existing production shafts. While the mineral at the newly discovered location was embedded much deeper than at the Charco Redondo's veins, the core samples showed nearly fifty percent of manganese content. Victor Daniels believed his discovery could be worth millions.

In spite of the warning issued by the CIA station chief in Santiago, Victor Daniels intended to keep the promise he made to Mary. He would have to move fast though. The moment Raul Castro received assurances from the State Department that the U.S. would negotiate with him the release of the hostages, the guerrilla kingpin could drag on the standoff for weeks, if not months.

As soon as the taking of the hostages was publicly known, Fidel rushed to detach himself from the kidnappings. In his nightly radio broadcast on Radio Rebelde, Castro denied any participation in the abductions, or having had prior knowledge of Raul's intended actions.

"Raul acted on his own as the commander of the Sierra del Cristal region," Fidel said, and then added, "however, the Americans are very good antiaircraft protection."

Eluding responsibilities had become Fidel's classic trademark.

The mastermind and manipulator of everything that took place during the insurgent war, and in the years that followed, Castro had a remarkable talent to lay the responsibility of his actions on others. The abduction of American civilians in the mining town of Moa, and that of unarmed sailors on leave from the U.S. base in Guantanamo, gave the Castro brothers their first significant victory against Batista's government. However, it had not been a triumph achieved in gallant combat, but one by way of sheer terror inflicted on innocent people and their families.

Victor Daniels spotted his friend Julio Tellechea seated at a table in a far corner of the spacious dining room. A renowned attorney in Santiago, Julio had once served as a cabinet member in the government and knew just about everyone in the city. The man was impeccably dressed in white drill 100 suit and an expensive Italian scarf in lieu of a tie. Victor Daniels noticed the tip of Julio's signature cigar protruding from his jacket pocket—a *Partagás*.

"Hello, Vic. How long has it been, ten months, a year maybe?"

"I've been away from paradise too long, Julio. It's good to see you again. Thanks for meeting me in such a short notice."

Julio flagged down the Maître d' and ordered cold beers and large servings of pitted olives and plantain chips.

"What brings you back to our peaceful Santiago de Cuba?"

"I love your sense of humor. I'm here because of the incident in Moa. My friend Raymond Elmore was one of the hostages taken by Raul Castro."

Julio took a quick look around to make sure that nobody was listening.

"I know Raymond very well. He's a nice guy. However, I expected something like this to happen sooner or later. The Castro brothers have a visceral hatred for all Americans and that includes you," added the attorney with a chuckle.

"I understand, Julio, and that's why I'm not going anywhere near the conflict area. My concern now is Raymond's family. That's the chief reason for my trip to Santiago"

"What do you have in mind?"

"Raymond's wife Mary is almost due to have her baby and this situation has her under a great deal of stress. She asked me to make contact with the rebels and offer them money for Raymond's release. There are ten thousand dollars on the table. Unofficially, of course, and definitely without the blessings of the American consul."

"Where do I fit in?"

"I presume that you could have connections within the rebel network in Santiago. You ought to know someone who could either send the word out, or deliver the money to Raul."

"Things have changed a lot around here, Vic. Batista's police and military intelligence assets are all over the place. Besides, most of my old acquaintances from the movement are either dead, in jail, or have joined the fight in the mountains. To complicate things further, the Army has blocked all access roads to the Sierras. Even if a messenger manages to get through, it will take him days to reach Raul's command post. And there are no guarantees that he would make it back, or that Raul would strike a deal. Raul could easily decide to keep the money and not release Raymond. Gangsters who subdue innocent people at gunpoint cannot be trusted."

"I can see a problem there."

"Any indications that Eisenhower might intervene militarily?"

The engineer shrugged. "Very unlikely. You are actually the third person I've heard asking that same question in the last two days. In all truth, the State Department is afraid that Raul may harm the hostages and has instructed the American consul in Santiago to start negotiating immediately. This has given the rebels carte blanche to milk the situation indefinitely."

"I blame most of what's happening here on that reporter from the New York Times, Matthews I think was his name. The guy did incalculable damage by misleading the Americans on who Fidel really is. In my opinion, he was another Neville Chamberlain. The articles he published in the Times gave the liberals in the State Department every argument possible to justify turning their backs on Batista."

"We are in for some troubled days."

"I agree. Batista is fighting with his hands tied behind his back. The Americans have blocked the delivery of fifteen training airplanes for the Cuban air force, and halted any future sales of arms, ammunition and spare parts destined for the Cuban army. There are twenty armored vehicles sitting somewhere in Florida waiting on an export license from the State Department, a license that you and I know will never get approved. The list goes on and on. Meanwhile, pro-Castro fund-raising organizations continue to collect money in the United States and send weapons and supplies to the rebels by air and sea. It seems like even the FBI is looking the other way. Some people in Washington can't wait to see Fidel Castro becoming Cuba's next dictator."

"What should I tell Mary?"

"Mary shouldn't worry. It is in Raul's best interest to keep the hostages healthy and not provoke a direct confrontation with the United States. If he harms one single hostage, Eisenhower will then have a perfect excuse to send in the Marines and Castro's days will be over. Tell Mary that her husband is not alone and probably playing poker and smoking a cigar in a mountain ranch as we speak."

Victor Daniels understood that, under the current circumstances, it would be impossible for him to gain Raymond's release. He decided to have an early lunch with Lloyd and Aida the next day, and then fly back to Havana.

The hostage situation at the Sierra del Cristal appeared to be headed toward a lengthy standoff. In a military communiqué at a later day, Raul announced that the hostages had been moved to multiple locations deep in the mountains, and that he intended to use them as human shields. The cease-fire had given the rebels plenty of time to regroup and restore the long-severed supply lines for weapons, ammunition, food and medical supplies.

Shortly after taking off from the airport in Santiago, Victor Daniels noticed a strong smell of gasoline. He had drained some of the gas from under the right wing to check for water and sediments during the routine pre-flight check. Had he left the valve open inadvertently? He didn't think so.

"Mayday, mayday. Santiago tower, this is Beechcraft 498. I need clearance for an emergency return to the airport."

After landing the Bonanza, a quick look under the wing revealed a thin stream of fuel gushing out of the tank drain valve. Victor Daniels was certain he had shut off the valve tightly before taking off. However, he recalled having seen two strangers standing on the ramp next to his airplane as he revved the engine. One of them could have easily crawled under the Bonanza's wing and opened the valve before he taxied away. Someone in Santiago wanted him dead.

In July of 1958, after weeks of negotiations between the State Department and Raul Castro, Raymond Elmore and the rest of the hostages were released by the rebels and airlifted by U.S. Navy helicopters to the naval base in Guantanamo.

Chapter 26

Not long after the rebels' victory of 1959, Castro's revolution began to suffer a systematic splintering within its ranks. Many rebel commanders believed that Fidel had betrayed the revolution and was negotiating secretly with the Kremlin to turn the island into a satellite of the Soviet Union. The consensus amongst a group of Castro's former allies was that those ideas were very dangerous indeed and that Fidel needed to go.

Castro moved swiftly to crack down on the seditions. His reaction forced many dissenting officers to scamper and regroup in the Escambray Mountains, where they joined a large group of local fighters who were waging a guerrilla war against the Marxist-leaning regime.

One of the early casualties from the fragmentation of Castro's top hierarchy was William Alexander Morgan, an American who had ranked up to commander of the rebel army while fighting in the Sierra Maestra. Disenchanted with the new direction the revolution had taken, Morgan joined the resistance and started running weapons and ammunition to the anti-Castro guerrilla forces in the Escambray.

In October of 1960, Morgan was arrested by the secret police, tried by a military court, and executed. Other high-ranking officers in the rebel army suffered the same fate as Morgan, or were sentenced to twenty years in prison. For many months, the man in charge of the military tribunals and executions at La Cabaña prison was no other than Ernesto Guevara, an Argentinean rebel commander known as *el Ché*. During Ché's tenure as chief of La Cabaña, the sound of the firing squad fusillade could be heard clearly outside the thick prison walls almost every night of the week.

Commander Camilo Cienfuegos, the third top man in Cuba's military hierarchy, was a charismatic rebel leader and a hero to most people in Cuba. Unfortunately for Camilo, he had become dangerously more popular than Fidel Castro himself. Less than a year after the guerrilla's victory, Camilo was also out of the picture.

Circumstantial evidence linked Camilo's disappearance to the arrest of Huber Matos, another dissident from Fidel Castro's inner-circle ranks. During the revolutionary war, Matos proved to be a great strategist and was credited with planning and executing the capture of Santiago de Cuba.

After the rebel takeover of Cuba, Castro placed Matos in command of the province of Camaguey. But like many of Fidel's closest allies, Matos became disillusioned and started making public speeches critical of Castro. He wanted the people to be aware of the dangers that an alliance with the Soviet Union would pose to everybody's freedoms.

Matos had often asked Castro to relieve him of his army command in Camaguey, a request that Fidel stonewalled. When Matos mentioned to Castro his concerns about the revolution turning communist, the kingpin reassured him that the ones flirting with Marxism were Raul and Ché, and not him. Fidel added that he had the situation under control.

It was then when Matos realized that Fidel was a compulsive liar and decided it was time for him to step down. In Matos' eyes, the commander-in-chief whom he had trusted and respected was nothing but a self-serving deceiver. The green revolution that Matos and many others had fought and died for had been betrayed.

Fidel Castro could not accept any of his close collaborators walking out on him. After learning that Matos had decided to step down, Castro ordered Camilo Cienfuegos to fly to Camaguey and place Matos under arrest. On that same day, Castro went on a televised rant against Matos accusing him of insubordination, and of leading an uprising against the people of Cuba.

Those who were close to commander Cienfuegos said that Camilo knew Matos had not committed treason. Upon his arrival in Camaguey, Camilo found Matos at home with his family and not up in arms in the mountains as Castro had insinuated. Camilo obeyed Castro's orders to place his friend under arrest, but did it only because he trusted Matos would receive a fair trial and ultimately be acquitted of all charges.

On October 28, 1959, at six in the evening, a twin-engine Cessna 310 plane took off from the city of Camaguey with pilot Luciano Fariñas at the controls. His two passengers were the popular commander Camilo Cienfuegos and his personal bodyguard. The plane never made it to Havana.

The search operation for Camilo's plane went on for several days. When all hope to find the aircraft, or survivors were lost, the Cuban government issued it's official report. The report stated that Camilo's Cessna 310 ran into bad weather en route to Havana and had likely crashed in the ocean.

Many people were skeptical of the government's version of Camilo's disappearance. The route from Camaguey to Havana was a straight line strictly above ground and the meteorological reports indicated that the weather had been fair on the day the plane vanished. No trace of the wreckage was ever found.

On December of 1959, Commander Hubert Matos was arbitrarily tried for treason by Castro's tribunals and sentenced to twenty years in prison.

THE LYNX

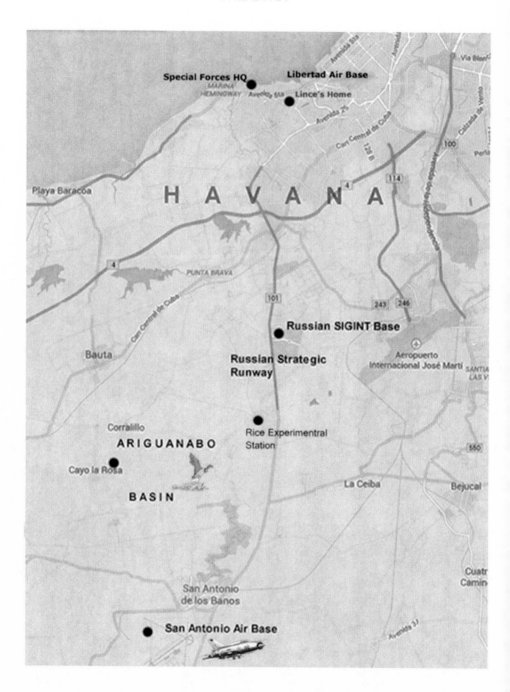

Map of Havana and vicinity, 1972

CVS-9 USS *Essex*, circa 1961. A4D-2 Skyhawks from the VA-34 Blue Blaster squadron were launched by the carrier in support of the Bay of Pigs invasion. The orders to engage Castro's air force never arrived. Archive photo.

AD-4 Skyhawk from the Blue Blasters squadron ready to launch from the USS Essex. April 1961. Archive photo

Soviet SS-4 medium-range ballistic missiles (NATO denomination R-12) similar to those deployed in Cuba in 1962. Archive photo.

Soviet TU-95 long range strategic bomber capable of delivering nuclear payloads. Archive photo.

Soviet Signals Intelligence base of Lourdes in Cuba.
Archive photo.

U2 Spy plane, similar to the one that was shot down
by Castro while conducting an unarmed reconnaissance mission
over Cuba in 1962. Archive Photo.

Skydivers gearing-up at Cayo la Rosa, 1973. The Piper Pawnee visible on the right was later on stolen by Cuban dissidents and flown to the United States. Photo courtesy of Peter Fandiño.

Aerial view of Cayo la Rosa airfield, 1973. Lake Ariguanabo in the background. Photo courtesy of Peter Fandiño.

David Edery. Accuracy landing event, Pan American Parachuting
Championships, Peru, 1975

Cuban Skydiving Team (partial) Peru, 1975. Front row from the
left: Guerra and Lince. Photo Courtesy of Tomás Berriolo
(standing, far right)

Captain Chuck Whittle, U.S. Army Golden Knights (left),
installs an experimental deployment device on Lince's (with
sunglasses) Russian UT-15 parachute. Collique, Peru. Photo SSG
Dave Goldie, Parachutist Magazine - August 1975.

Lince's copy of Skies Call. He used the book to teach himself,
and his teammates in Cuba the art of free fall skydiving.

Lince (left) with Canadian skydivers Gabriel and Derek next to a AN-2
jump plane. San Nicolas de Bari, 1976. Courtesy of J.P.

Cubana Airlines Viscount, similar to the one hijacked en route from
Miami to Varadero on November 1, 1958. It was the first hijacking ever in
U.S. aviation history. Archive photo.

Lince's home in the neighborhood of Siboney, La Habana

Lince with his parents, Ramona and Victor Daniels Nickolich,
Havana, 1976. Courtesy of J.P.

Part III

THE STING

Chapter 27

You'll never find a better sparring partner than adversity.
— *Golda Meir*

Havana, November 15, 1977

"Luciano left an hour ago to take care of some unexpected business," Ana Maria told Nick. "But two comrades from the Ministry of Interior are waiting for you inside." Ana Maria's unblinking stare warned Lince to expect trouble ahead.

"Thanks, Ana Maria. It's good to see you again."

Lince sighed in relief when Marcos dropped him off at the club headquarters and not in the Villa Maristas detention center as he had feared. Nonetheless, that momentary respite vanished when he learned that the agents were waiting for him there.

Lince found Lieutenant Tony Angulo seated at Luciano's mahogany desk. The lieutenant dressed casually in a short-sleeved checkered shirt and slacks. In all those years, he had never seen him out of his signature olive-drab uniform and gun belt. Next to Tony stood a lanky man he had never met before, also wearing civilian attire.

"Good afternoon, Nick. This is Comrade Lazo, a fellow officer from the DSE."

Lince took a step forward to shake hands with Lazo, and then with Angulo.

"Is the team ready for another victory at the Pan Americans?" Lazo asked him.

"We were heading in that direction until about noon today. Now I'm not so sure."

"A very unusual situation has just come up."

"What's going on?"

"There is an American in Havana trying to contact you."

"An American trying to contact me? You must be kidding me."

Angulo locked his steely green eyes on the skydiver. "We are not in the business of joking around, comrade."

"What does this person want from me?"

"That's exactly what we are trying to find out. Have you ever told anyone that you want to leave Cuba?"

Lince took a deep breath. Angulo and Lazo definitely knew something. The question was how much. He decided it was time to get on the offensive.

"Negative, comrade. This makes me angry. I admit that I have been rebellious in the past, but I love my country and the revolution. Everything that matters to me is right here. I would never abandon Cuba, or my family for that matter."

"Then you should be cleared of any wrongdoing once we get to the bottom of this, correct?"

"You can count on it, comrades. What am I supposed to do?"

"This is what you need to do. Go home now and wait for this man to contact you. If and when he does, act friendly and find out exactly what he wants. And make sure not to mention a word of this to anyone, not even to your parents."

Angulo handed him a piece of paper with a telephone number written on it.

"You can reach us at this number. If the American calls you within the next few days and what he wants with you is inconsequential, we may still have time to send you to compete with the team in Mexico. Until then, however, we consider this a very serious matter. The revolution is counting on your full cooperation."

Lince left Luciano's office with the sinking feeling he had reached the end of the line. If it was true that an American was in Havana trying to reach him that could only mean one thing—the State Department had acted upon the call for help he sent out ten months earlier with his Canadian friends. In hindsight, he decided the whole thing had been a terrible mistake.

Why had Angulo asked him if he ever told anyone that he wanted to leave Cuba? It was obvious the officer knew much more than he have told Lince and had tried to catch him off guard.

On his way home, Lince thought of making another attempt to escape from the island. He still had one large tractor inner tube hidden in his backyard shed that he had stolen from the rice research station. He had anticipated that someday he might be forced to make another desperate attempt by sea.

But it was late November, probably the worst time of the year to sail to Florida on a raft made from one inner tube and no engine. The prevailing winds that gusted from the northeast would never let him get past the first shallow reefs.

Also, he had to expect the DSE would place his house under a twenty-four-hour surveillance. Painted into a corner, Lince had just one option left—keep a cool head and trust his gut instincts. That would likely be the last mind game he would get to play against the Cuban intelligence services ever. His odds did not look good, though.

Lince thought that a prayer or two might help him now, but the Communists had long made him forget how to talk to God.

"On a stormy sea of moving emotion, Tossed about, I'm like a ship on the ocean..."

The Zenith trans-oceanic radio brought on the beat of Kansas marred by a barely perceptible static. The melody of *Carry on Wayward Son* rode the airwaves all the way from Little Rock, Arkansas, transcending both atmospheric hurdles and a deliberate interference by the Cuban government. Like with the VOA, the intrusion was a deep hum parked at the station's frequency—a wacky annoyance that Lince could fix with a small tweak of the dial.

Lince's favorite program on KAAY was the Beaker Street show, a commercial-free medley featuring the Eagles, the Who, Steppenwolf, King Crimson, Led Zeppelin and many other popular bands. The radio signal would get progressively sharper into the late hours of the evening, and then fade away just before sunrise. Along with the music came a subtle message. There was a parallel universe where people could express themselves without boundaries.

At eight o'clock that evening, the sudden ringing of the telephone startled him. He turned down the volume on the radio and lifted the handset.

"Hello", he answered.

"May I speak to Nick, please?" The man at the other end of the line had spoken in flawless English.

"Nick speaking."

"Nick, I'm an American in transit. I'm calling from a pay phone and don't have much time. I have a message for you. Do you have a pencil and paper handy?"

"Sure." Lince grabbed a ballpoint pen from the desk drawer and drew near an old issue of *Paris Match* magazine.

"Please write down the following phone number in Mexico City." The man spelled out all nine digits twice.

"Can you please read those numbers back to me?"

One by one, Lince read back to the man the numbers he had jotted down on the magazine cover.

"You've got it. When you get to Mexico, call that number and ask for Mr. Duvalón. Ask him if he has parachutes for sale. He will give you an address."

"Sir, who are you?"

"I'm just a messenger. I have to go now. Good-bye and good luck to you."

The line went dead. Lince kept the receiver pressed against his ear for a few more seconds. However, he did not hear the secondary click that would have revealed the call had been listened to. The DSE probably had the most undetectable phone tapping devices in existence.

Lince released the phone dual buttons and dialed the number that Lieutenant Angulo had given him at Luciano's office earlier that day. Lazo answered the call after one ring.

"The stranger you guys told me about just called a minute ago." He gave Lazo, word by word, the Spanish version of the entire conversation he just had with the presumed American.

"I have no clue who that man was, or why he would give me that information," he added.

"That's interesting," Lazo said. Give us some time to look into this. For the time being, don't leave your house. We'll get back to you in a day or two."

Lince was baffled. Why would a bona fide U.S. government agent be so careless as to allow the DSE snoops to find his home phone number among his belongings, as Lince now suspected was the case? Still, the Cuban intelligence could have learned of the agent's intentions through other means.

Could it be possible for the anonymous caller to be one of the State Department officials now working at the U.S. Special Interest mission in Havana? It would make sense for the U.S. government to use one of their assets already inside Cuba. Nonetheless, the agent had made a huge blunder by delivering the coded message over the phone. Any foreign operative conducting a mission in Cuba would know that most phone calls on the island were monitored by the intelligence services. The man should have avoided giving him any compromising information over the phone. As an alternative, he could have told Lince that he was a friend of a friend and arrange to meet him somewhere in the city, perhaps in a park, at the beach, or in a movie theater.

Lince had hoped for the American Embassy in Mexico to contact him secretly after his arrival in that country, but he never expected the U.S. to send someone to Cuba ahead of his trip with the key to facilitate his escape. As a result of the gaffe, the Cuban intelligence knew he had been given the means to defect during the upcoming trip to Mexico. That would be something rather difficult to explain to both Angulo and Lazo.

The plan itself was clever, though Once in Mexico, all he needed was to find a payphone and call Duvalón. He would ask the man if he had parachutes for sale—the coded question that only Lince would know.

Duvalón, in turn, would give him an address to a safe place in Mexico City. It would then be up to Lince to break away from the team's security, find some means of transportation and reach the agreed-upon location.

Meanwhile, Lazo had decided to keep him under house arrest and not take him to a detention center. But for how long? Back in Luciano's office, Angulo mentioned that he could still be sent to compete in Mexico. Would his key position in the skydiving team be a factor on whether or not he would walk free? The whole thing was an unsolvable riddle, at least for the time being.

Miracles happen, his mother often told him.

Using a simple encryption code he remembered from a spy novel, Lince wrote down Duvalón's phone number backwards and in two columns on the corner of the Paris Match magazine. He tore off the piece of paper and folded it tightly into a small wad. He then pulled out the center drawer of his desk and ran the tip of his fingers on the underside surface of the desktop—feeling for a familiar crack in the wood. When he found it, he pressed the wad of paper into the fracture and slid the drawer back in place.

Music had always soothed his soul during the most trying moments in his life. He reached for the radio and turned the volume back up, only much louder this time around. The chords of *Midnight Rider* started vibrating against the walls in the study and seeping into every cell of his body. His parents, aware of his predicament, would understand his mood. He kicked back in his recliner, closed his eyes and hoped the evening would never end. Lince heard his mother walking into the study, but kept his eyes closed. The most wonderful lady in his life put a pillow under his head, turned off the radio and placed a gentle kiss on his forehead. He slept soundly all night long until the first light came in through the half-open blinds.

When he woke up, he still had a glimmer of hope that the nightmare he had lived during the past twenty-four hours was just that—a fleeting nightmare. That's when he noticed the missing corner from the copy of *Paris Match* magazine.

He thought of going for a run around the block, but then remembered he was under house detention. All morning long, Lince paced nervously around the house waiting for either Lazo's phone call, or for the doorbell to ring and announce his imminent arrest by State Security operatives.

Chapter 28

By way of deception, thou shalt do war.

— *The Mossad*

The house phone rang at one o'clock in the afternoon. It was Lazo.

"Nick, my superiors would like to have a word with you. We have set a meeting for three o'clock this afternoon."

Lazo gave Lince an address in the district of La Rampa in El Vedado. La Rampa was a broad, avenue on Twenty-Third Street that stretched from Avenida L all the way to the Malecón waterfront. It was the setting for several landmark buildings including the *Habana Libre* hotel—formerly known as Habana Hilton—the *Pabellón Cuba* exhibition center, and *Radiocentro*, a large theater that once featured Cinerama-formatted movies on a seventy-foot screen. Having renamed just about everything else in Cuba, the Communists had also changed the theater's name. *Radiocentro* was now known as *Cine Yara*.

Lince left his house without telling his parents whom he intended to meet, and uncertain if he would ever return home. It was a cloudless day with a cool breeze that brought the fresh scent of the ocean far inland. On his way to his daunting rendezvous with the DSE, Lince kept telling himself to stay relaxed and deny anything that could incriminate him. While the trauma of the last twenty-four hours still weighed heavily on him, he was surprisingly calm and felt no fear.

The skydiver halted in front of a nondescript wooden door facing Twenty-Third Street. A small metal plate fastened to the frame matched the number that Lazo had given him over the phone. He rang the bell.

Seconds later, he heard a deadbolt click and the door opened inwards a few inches. He pushed the door and stepped into a small landing that led to a narrow and steep stairwell. Standing at the top of the stairs was Lazo, still holding in his hand the thin rope he had used to release the front door's locking mechanism. The officer gestured him to walk upstairs.

Half the way up, Lince heard the door closing behind him with a solid thump. Under different circumstances, he would have felt like trapped inside a cage. But now it didn't make much difference. There was no way out of the island either. All he could do now was to summon his wits and keep a cool head.

It's just a mind game, he kept telling himself.
Lazo greeted him on top of the stairs with a handshake and ushered him into a large room with high ceilings and aging plastered walls. The place reeked of mildew and everything from floor to ceiling revealed the unkind passage of time. Two tall windows facing the street had been shaded off with several coats of white paint.

The only light in the room came from two fluorescent bulbs on the ceiling, one of them flickering intermittently in its bare fixture. Lince wondered how many unsuspecting victims had been brought to that same room over the years for interrogation, or even torture and death.

He found three strangers dressed in civilian clothes seated at a long wooden table. It was the first time Lince had seen any of them in his life. The men looked older, more serious and more dreadful than both Angulo and Lazo. *Cuban counterintelligence.* All three men rose briefly from their chairs to shake hands with Lince, but only one stated his name and rank.

"I'm Colonel Mendez from the State Security." The man gestured Lince to take a chair opposite to him.

Mendez physical appearance was staggering. His face was weather-beaten, inscrutable and deeply scarred from an early youth acne. But what surprised Lince the most wasn't Mendez' harsh facial features, but the manner in which he spoke. The colonel had addressed him in a cultured Spanish with a calm and polite tone of voice untypical of agents from the secret police.

Because of this, Lince guessed that the colonel had received a higher education outside Cuba, perhaps at the Stasi academy in East Germany or the KGB Institute in Moscow. Not many officers in the Ministry of Interior had reached the rank of colonel, which meant that Mendez had to be a very dangerous man indeed.

Mendez leaned back in his chair and looked at Lince straight in the eyes.

"I've been told that you had a phone conversation with an American last night."

"Yes, someone claiming to be an American called my house around eight."

"Who do you think gave this American your name and phone number?"

Lince made a puzzled gesture and shrugged.

"Honestly, I have no clue. I haven't stopped thinking about this whole thing since last night. The only explanation I came up with is that my sister Militza might be behind this strange episode.

"As you probably know, she left for the United States more than ten years ago."

Mendez was silent for a few seconds, trying to grasp the significance of Lince's words.

"What do you mean? How would your sister know that you would be travelling with the parachute team to Mexico? Did you tell her?"

"Not me. I haven't spoken to her in years. But my parents could have mentioned about my trip when she called our home a few weeks ago."

"Why would your sister ask someone to give you a coded message and a telephone number for you to call in Mexico City? Wouldn't that be very strange?"

"I can't answer that, Colonel. Perhaps she's trying to find a way to see me again. My parents said that she always sounds homesick and cries when she calls home. It's possible that she wants to send my parents a package with clothing or something else. Militza lived in Mexico City for over a year after she left Cuba. She probably still has friends there."

"Tell me Nick, would you like to see your sister again?"

"Not really," he lied. "She was the one who left us. I don't think she understands that I'm totally committed to the cause of the revolution."

"Who else knew that you were going to Mexico?" the man seated to the right of Mendez asked.

"I haven't told many people outside my immediate family, just a few close friends. But everyone in the skydiving club knows.

Besides, the news of who makes the national sports teams travels very fast here."

"How often does your sister call Cuba?" the third man intervened.

Lince was sure that the man already knew the answer. The DSE eavesdroppers had been monitoring his home phone for years.

"My parents have told me that she calls about twice a month, sometimes more often."

"Nick, I want you to think way back. Think of the time when you traveled to Hungary and Peru with the team. Did your parents give you any letters to mail to your sister in the United States?"

"Certainly not, comrade."

"Did you hand over any correspondence to the U.S. Army guys in Peru?

"Absolutely not."

What else do these people know? Lince wondered.

"Did you say anything unusual to the Canadians who visited the parachute club late last year? We know that you spent time alone with them."

That last question was posed nonchalantly, but it hit Lince like a ton of bricks. He felt four pairs of eyes weighing down on him— waiting for his reaction. Evidently, Mendez suspected there was a connection between the American's presence in Havana and Gabriel and Derek's visit.

"Absolutely not, comrade. I would never do such a thing."

Mendez exchanged glances with the other DSE officers and got up from his chair.

"Very well. My comrades and I will have a private talk now. It won't take too long. You may wait for us outside."

Lince could not remember how long he sat in that narrow foyer, feeling like a defendant waiting on a jury's verdict. It could have been ten, twenty minutes or maybe even an hour. His sudden inspiration to bring his sister into the equation appeared to have thrown Mendez off balance momentarily, but the State Security colonel definitely knew more than he cared to reveal. Mendez could have made a great poker player.

He told himself to stay calm and not show any emotions. There probably was a hidden video camera somewhere in the foyer, perhaps behind the lone picture that hung slightly crooked on the wall facing him.

The skydiver had seen that picture before. It was an eight-by-ten black-and-white portrait of Ché Guevara holding a machete in a sugar cane field—one of Ché's iconic photos taken in the early days of the revolution for propaganda purposes.

Lince thoughts took him back to the day when he met Ché Guevara's daughter Hildita at a birthday party in his house. The celebration was in honor of Juan Luis Vasquez, a Chilean student who lived as a house guest with Nick's family. Juan Luis was part of a group of one hundred medical students sent to Cuba by Marxist president Salvador Allende before the bloody coup of September 1973. The change in Chile's political scenario had made it impossible for the medical students return to their country. They all feared persecution from the government of Augusto Pinochet for having lived and studied in Cuba. Juan Luis had now found a home with Lince's family in Cuba.

Hildita Guevara de Gadea was a lovely eighteen-year-old lady with jet-black hair and big eyes. She had become good friends with several of the Chilean women who were studying medicine in Cuba. During the party, Lince invited Hildita and her friends to go and watch him skydive at Cayo la Rosa.

The following weekend, a few Chilean students showed up at the drop zone accompanied by Hildita Guevara. But within minutes of the group's arrival Lince was assailed by Guerra, one of the Communist Party commissars.

"Lince, don't get any ideas about Ché's daughter," Guerra warned him. "She's a dear protégée of the Cuban revolution. I can assure you that you will get in serious trouble."

That was the last time Lince saw Ché's daughter. She never showed up again at his home with her Chilean friends. Hildita just disappeared from the radar.

The door in the foyer opened without a warning. It was Lazo.

"You can come in now, comrade," Lazo said.

Lince stepped back into the room and sat on the same chair.

"Comrade Nickolich, is there anything else you would like to add to what you already told us?" Mendez asked him.

"No, nothing that I can think of."

"Very well. We believe you have told us the truth."

Lince could not believe his ears. He nodded once and smiled.

"You have earned your place in the skydiving team and at this time we see no further reason to keep you from traveling to Mexico. We trust that you will represent Cuba with honor at the Pan American Games and score a victory for the motherland."

"In the next day or so, Comrade Lazo will summon the members of the skydiving delegation to explain the circumstances of your temporary separation from the team. He will tell them that there were some false accusations made against you, but that you have been cleared of any wrongdoing. As for the call from the American, it's critical that you don't mention that episode to anyone."

"I understand Comrade Mendez. Thank you."

Lazo walked over to Lince's side of the table and placed a typewritten sheet of paper and a pen in front of the skydiver.

"Please read this carefully. It's the exact same document that you signed at the drop zone earlier this week. We just added a few sentences to it."

The paper in front of Lince was the contract the DSE would not hesitate to use against him if he were to violate any of the rules listed therein. All the standard mandates were there; never be alone, never make phone calls, never accept gifts from strangers, never take a taxi or public transportation, and defend the honor of Fidel Castro and the revolution with violence if necessary.

A paragraph had been added at the bottom of the page. It ordered Lince to report to the head of the delegation if someone in Mexico approached him with anything unusual, and strictly forbade him from calling or writing his sister or any other person, either in Mexico or in the United States. The skydiver signed the document and gave it back to Lazo.

"There is one more thing, Comrade Nickolich," Mendez added. "Forget the phone number the American gave you. Erase it from your memory. And don't let anyone talk you into staying in Mexico." Mendez took a long and deliberate pause.

"You should know that we have the means to find you anywhere in the world."

"That will never happen, comrade."

Lince knew that Mendez had actually meant *don't think for a moment that you have fooled us.*

The skydiver stood up, shook hands with the three men and followed Lazo out of the room.

Lince was halfway down the stairs when he noticed the rope on the wall next to him tensing up, followed by the sound of the front door getting unlocked. The door swung open a few inches allowing the afternoon sun to shine in. He could not remember ever being so happy to see the light of day.

The counterintelligence officers upstairs had to know he was lying. There was only one plausible explanation why he had been allowed to walk out of that place a free man and get reinstated in the skydiving team. It had to do with Castro's egocentric mind. The Cuban government believed their skydiving team could defeat the U.S. Army at the Pan American skydiving games this time around. That victory, however, would not be possible if he was not on the team.

Sport parachuting was the only arena in which Cuba might have a chance to score a victory against the U.S. military. Such a triumph in Mexico would be a huge accomplishment of the communist revolution, and particularly for the chronically anti-American Fidel. Castro's delusions of grandeur had just handed Lince his ticket to freedom.

Within seconds, Colonel Mendez had given Lince two conflicting messages. First, he told him that he enjoyed their full trust and confidence, something Lince didn't believe for retribution if he ever decided to escape. There was no doubt in his mind that the DGI would keep a tight watch on him from the moment he stepped off the plane in Mexico City.

He wondered if Colonel Kleber Marti or the de la Guardia twins had already been informed of his latest quandary. But as of now, the day of reckoning had been postponed until his return from Mexico.

Lince knew then and there that regardless of the obstacles he might encounter in the forthcoming days, he would have to follow one fundamental rule to a tee.

Thou shalt never return.

On the evening of November 21, 1977, the skydiving delegation walked out the José Marti Airport building to board the Cubana Airlines IL-62 that would fly them to Mexico City. Everyone was there but Lince. Just minutes before the final boarding call, the team leader pulled the skydiver aside and gave him the bad news.

"Lince, unfortunately we don't have your passport. The courier who brought our documents said that Minister Lussón left town on vacation without signing your travel authorization."

"What's the problem?"

"I think it had to do with your last minute reinstatement in the team. Unfortunately, they could not reach Lussón on time."

"What am I supposed to do?"

"There is a Mexicana Airlines flight leaving for Mexico City in three days. The Foreign Service will dispatch a courier to Pinar del Rio tomorrow to find Lussón and get your papers signed. I have been given assurances that everything will be ready on time for you to catch the Mexicana flight. We look forward to seeing you in Mexico City on Wednesday night."

Lince hid his disappointment behind a forged smile and bid good-bye to his teammates. There would be plenty of time during the taxi ride home to digest what had just transpired. He found it hard to believe that Lussón had failed to sign his documents only because he was out of reach.

The skydiver was convinced that Colonel Mendez had intentionally delayed his trip to Mexico to buy himself more time. Mendez could still be waiting for some conclusive information from his sources that would prove Lince had indeed contacted the American government for help. His ordeal with the DSE was far from over. Many things could still happen in three days.

Back at home, Lince reassured his parents that everything was going to be fine.

"Apparently, the club could not get my papers ready on time for today's departure. However, Mejias assured me that I will make it on the next flight out to Mexico City leaving on Wednesday night."

Lince noticed a shadow of skepticism clouding his parents' eyes, but neither of them uttered a word of discouragement. For good luck, he had left his packed suitcase on the spiral staircase landing by the front door.

Two days later, a man from the Ministry of Foreign Affairs called him at home.

"Comrade, Minister Lussón has signed your travel documents. Everything is now in order for your trip to Mexico."

"That's great news."

"We booked you on the Mexicana flight that leaves at eight o'clock tomorrow evening. A courier will be at your house at seven in the morning. He will deliver both your passport, and the airline ticket."

The next morning, Lince got out of bed at five thirty feeling like a million dollars. The temperature was sixty-five degrees Fahrenheit under clear skies. It was a perfect day for a workout.

He started his routine with a few sets of pushups and sit-ups, then strapped himself to the old parachute harness that still hung from a mango tree branch. It was the device he often used to practice his acrobatic drills at home. Like he'd done hundreds of times before, Lince closed his eyes and imagined himself in free fall accelerating to over one hundred miles per hour. He tucked-in his knees, dipped his shoulder and turn the palm of his hands to simulate deflecting the wind and performing the flat turns.

In an actual skydive, it usually took him less than a second to complete a full 360-degree turn in one direction. A full series included two flat turns in opposite directions, a back loop, two more opposing flat turns and one final back loop before opening his parachute. All the maneuvers had to be complete and in perfect alignment with a large arrow marked on the ground. Equipped with powerful binoculars, the judges timed the series from start to finish and added penalties if a turn was made short of 360 degrees, or if a back loop was performed off heading. To win a medal in the international arena, a skydiver needed to complete a clean style series within the six to seven seconds range. Lince was now very close to reaching that coveted mark.

Lince had been in the harness for a good half hour when he heard his mother calling from the kitchen. The coffee was ready. He unstrapped himself from the harness and walked back into the house, held his mother softly by the shoulders and kissed her on the cheek. He wondered when he might see her again and sensed that she knew he wasn't coming back this time around. There was no need for words. The two tears he saw escaping from her emerald-green eyes had spoken with enough eloquence.

He sliced a piece of Cuban bread in half and placed it in the toaster oven, then poured a hefty dose of strong coffee to a cup of warm milk and stirred in a spoonful of sugar. When the bread turned golden, he buttered both slices and took everything on a tray to *la terraza*, his favorite room in the house.[12]

Victor Daniels had designed the five-hundred-square-foot enclosed terrace with one thought in mind. With the tall glass windows open, the predominantly northeastern breeze that blew on that side of the island would provide a natural cooling to the circular room. The windows also offered a two hundred and seventy degree panoramic view of the street ahead and the surrounding gardens.

A wooden partition that divided the room from the wet bar now served as a display for a collection of skydiving medals, pictures and diplomas that Lince had won over the years. Every item that hung on that wall brought a particular memory to his mind, all of them linked to a certain time and place. That morning, Lince saw those past triumphs as pieces of a large jigsaw puzzle that symbolized his long skydiving journey.

---

[12] Page 242

The puzzle was now almost complete but for one last piece, the piece that he hoped would be waiting for him in Mexico. From the terrace's lookout, Lince watched an Alfa-Romeo sedan making a sharp s-turn into his driveway. A quick glance at his watch showed one minute to seven o'clock. The courier from the Foreign Ministry was exactly on time.

"Comrade Nickolich?" the man at the front door asked him.
"That's me."
"I work for the Foreign Relations Ministry. I brought you the travel documents for your trip to Mexico."
"Thank you. May I offer you a cup of coffee?"
"Thanks, but I don't have time. I must get back to the office."
The man handed Lince an unsealed manila envelope. A quick glance inside revealed it contained his official Cuban passport and the Mexicana Airlines ticket.
"Your flight leaves at eight o'clock tonight. Do you need transportation to the airport?"
"No, thanks. A friend already offered to give me a ride."
"Good luck to you in the competition."
The courier rushed back to his car, backed out of the driveway and sped away with a swift shifting of gears.

Lince returned to the terrace, took the passport and airline ticket out of the envelope and placed them on a glass top table. No words could describe the deep relief he felt at that very moment.

"I see that you are traveling to Mexico after all." His father had followed him quietly into the terrace.

"Yes, Dad. I'll be back in just two weeks, hopefully with a medal or two hanging from my neck. Do you still need the reading glasses we talked about?"

Lince placed his index finger in front of his lips and then drew an imaginary circle in the air. He did that to remind his father that there could be microphones planted in the house.

"Son, I would like the glasses. But only if you have a few dollars to spare."

Lince knew in his heart that his parents were secretly counting on him. He was the only hope they had left to get out of the cursed island.

On the other hand, they were probably worried sick of what might happen to him if something went wrong along the way.

Chapter 29

The ride to the airport in Vicente's 1957 Chevy was similar to the one they took three days earlier, only slower this time due to a few rain showers they encountered along the way. Other than for the odd size carburetor under the hood taken from a Russian jeep, the Chevy Bel-Air was no different from the automobile that rolled out of a Detroit assembly line twenty years earlier. The cherry-red paint almost had its original shine and all chrome trims, bumpers, and hubcaps still reflected the setting sun with a blinding glare. The American cars that cruised on the streets of Cuba were a powerful testimony of both pride and ingenuity in the face of overwhelming adversities.

Victor Daniels and Vicente had been good friends since the days Vicente used to own a nursery that supplied most of the fruit and ornamental trees in the Biltmore. But like all other businesses on the island, Vicente's nursery was confiscated without compensation. To make ends meet, the man did odd jobs and ran errands for families in the neighborhood. He was a quiet and kind person who never refused to do a favor.

The rain stopped and Lince rolled down his window to let in the fresh breeze and enjoy an amazing sunset unveiling in the horizon. At six-thirty that evening, Vicente made a right turn onto the road to the main terminal building at the international airport in Rancho Boyeros. The man brought the Chevy to a halt in front of the terminal building and turned off the engine.

"Nick, I'll wait here until your flight takes off."

"Thank you, my friend. But you should not worry about me. I think Fidel has finally decided to let me fly."

Vicente stepped out of the car with an agility uncommon in a man of his age and took the suitcase from the trunk. He then tipped his straw cowboy hat at Lince in his distinctive friendly gesture.

"All the best to you, Nick. Or should I call you *el Lince*?"

The skydiver laughed. "Lince is fine, Vicente. I'll see you around."

The young man stood at the curb waving his hand as the vintage automobile glided quietly toward the airport exit. Lince realized that after all those years he never got to know the man's last name. To him, he was just *Vicente*.

In 1977, the airport serving Havana looked pretty much like it did in the late fifties when his family drove there to say good-bye to Victor Daniels on his long business trips. Not many renovations had been done since and the building was badly in need of repair. The superb infrastructure the Castro's inherited from the Batista government had suffered almost two-decades of abuse and total neglect. The international airport in Rancho Boyeros was not an exemption to the rule.

Instead of Aerovias Q, TWA, Pan Am, National, Delta and BOAC, the signs above the counters now read Aeroflot, Mexicana, Iberia, CZA, and Air Canada. Most flights in and out of the international terminal came in and left with many empty seats for obvious reasons. The average Cuban citizen was not allowed to travel outside of the island. At that time, foreign tourism was very restricted if not discouraged. Castro believed it was a good thing to keep the Cuban people from interacting with the rest of the world.

International travel in and out of the José Martí airport was limited to Cuban government officials, foreign diplomats, Soviet bloc engineers and technicians, members of Cuban official delegations and a small number of foreign tourists—most of them from Mexico and Canada. And there was the steady trickle of immigrants outside the military age who continued to leave the country via Spain and Mexico.

The airport was also the departure point for scores of spies and diplomatic couriers dispatched by the Directorate of General Intelligence to Cuban embassies and commercial offices throughout the world. Castro's secret army of instigators, saboteurs, and radical ideologues went on to roam the capitals of the free world spreading their poisonous ideology with diplomatic immunity.

Twelve years earlier, arguably one of the most relevant personalities of the regime's hierarchy was spirited out the island from that airport under a thick cloak of secrecy. Clean-shaven and disguised in a business suit, the thirty-some year old man boarded a scheduled commercial flight from Havana to Madrid. The inconspicuous man had a false passport from the Republic of Uruguay under the name of Adolfo Mena Gonzalez. After landing in Madrid, the man continued his long and incognito journey that would eventually take it to Bolivia.

With the mindset to topple the regime of General René Barrientos and establish a Marxist regime by way of guerrilla warfare, Ernesto *Ché* Guevara had left for his final rendezvous with destiny in the rugged mountains of Bolivia. From that day on until his death, Ché would be known by the code name *Ramón*.

After Ché was captured and killed by Bolivian Special Forces, Castro mandated a perennial state of mourning in Cuba. The first casualty after Ché's fall were the religious holidays—there would be no more Christmas celebrations on the island. Gone with Ché and Christmas were the traditional Spanish nougats, the roasted leg of pork and the bottle of red wine the Cuban families were previously allowed to buy to celebrate the traditional festivities.

No more Ché, no more Christmas and no more vino.

Lince placed his suitcase on the scale at the curbside Mexicana counter, where an agent promptly stapled a receipt to the back of his airline ticket. That's when a familiar voice startled him from behind.

"You didn't think you could leave without saying goodbye, Lince?"

Lince turned around to face Nestor Aponte, the head instructor at the skydiving club. In his eyes, Aponte was a good-hearted person, but nonetheless a radicalized fanatic who could not find a blemish in either Castro or the Marxist doctrine. Whenever he was involved in a political discussion, Aponte always raised his voice above the rest as if trying to prove he was more loyal to the regime than the others. Lince suspected the man was trying to redeem himself in the eyes of the regime. Rumor had it that a dark secret in his past prevented him from traveling to skydiving events abroad.

"What a nice surprise. That was very thoughtful of you to drive all the way here just to send me off."

"No sweat, Lince. I just wanted to remind you that this competition means a lot to all of us."

"Well, it also means a lot to me, Aponte."

"We are counting on you. Beating the Americans would be a huge victory for the revolution."

"Of course it will be. You will not be disappointed. But I must go now and find my gate. I already missed a flight three days ago and definitely don't want to miss this one," he said with a chuckle.

Lince found the dimly lit international departure gate nearly deserted. There were less than twenty people in the room waiting to board the evening flight to Mexico City. He walked up to the immigration counter and handed his passport and ticket to an agent dressed in well-pressed army fatigues. The man inspected the documents and told him to take a seat. Lince eyed an empty bench against the back wall and took the seat on the far right.

Two rows ahead of him was a man dressed in a colorful matching tunic and Kufi whom Lince guessed was a diplomat from either Sudan or Nigeria. Next to the shuttered windows, a young Scandinavian couple struggled to keep a rowdy boy under control. The boy of seven or eight years, with sandy blond hair appeared determined to break free from his mother's steely grip while uttering groans of contempt.

A true Viking in the making, Lince thought.

Lince went on to study all the other passengers in the room, but nobody there seemed to fit the profile of a DSE agent. It seemed odd that the State Security would allow him to travel out of the country without an escort on a foreign flag airline. As far as he knew, that never happened.

Lince was in the process of scanning the room for the second time trying to identify his would-be bodyguard when he heard his name called over the loudspeakers.

"Mexico City passenger Nickolich please return to the immigration desk."

The skydiver felt his pulse racing. Had Colonel Mendez decided to pull him off the flight at the very last moment?

Keep your cool and don't show any sign of anxiety, he told himself.

He had heard of outbound passengers at the Jose Marti airport being recalled at the last moment prior to boarding a plane out of Cuba only to learn they were no longer on the flight manifest. Bracing himself for another unpleasant episode, he got up from his seat and walked up to the immigration counter. The same officer was waiting for him unfazed.

"Comrade Nickolich?"

"I am Victor Nickolich."

"We forgot to give you your boarding pass." The man handed the skydiver a white boarding card while locking his gaze on Lince's eyes. "Have a nice flight."

"Thank you." Lince placed the boarding card in his blazer pocket and returned to his seat.

Lince took a deep breath. The withholding of the boarding card had not been accidental, but a fear-inducing tactic by the secret police. He believed Mendez had used the alleged oversight to send him another subtle message—*don't forget we are still in control of your life.* Lince could picture the Colonel seated behind the wheel of his Alfa Romeo by the airport terminal—his secure mobile telephone within hand's reach and waiting for the call that would justify pulling the skydiver off the flight. The mind game was far from over.

It was already dark outside when a flight attendant closed and armed the front door of the Mexicana Boeing 737. The stewardess lifted a phone handset off its cradle to make the flight safety announcement. In the cockpit, the pilot revved up the jet engines and begun the slow taxi run toward the runway.

Another flight attendant stopped by to check Lince's seatbelt and wished him a good flight.

Halfway down the runway, the airplane pitched upwards at a steep angle and took off from Cuban soil. From his window, Lince watched the city lights get dimmer and soon disappear as the jet climbed past a layer of broken clouds. He said a silent adieu to a country he didn't expect to set foot in again, at least not until it was free.

At some point during the flight, Lince put his hand in his jean's pocket and felt for a small seam at the bottom. That's where he had sewn-in the piece of paper with Duvalón's phone number written in code. He had no idea how things would play out, only that he would not let anyone stop him this time around. Providence had just given him one last chance—a chance he was determined not to waste.

THE LYNX

Chapter 30

The truest wisdom is a resolute determination.
— Napoleon Bonaparte

Mexicana flight 302 touched down in the Aztec capital at five minutes after ten in the evening, local time in Mexico DF. There, the foot soldiers and their mean German shepherd dogs that patrolled the Cuban shoreline no longer posed a threat to him. Neither were the neighborhood snitches, the torpedo boats, or the MIG jet fighters. From that moment on, the only obstacles between him and his freedom would be the DSE agents embedded in his team, the DGI operatives stationed at the Cuban Embassy in Mexico City, and his own nerve.

He found Mejias and two men in dark suits waiting for him outside the passport control area. Mejias introduced the strangers as employees from the Cuban Embassy.

"Glad you made it, Lince. Did you have a good flight?"

"Yes, and much shorter than I had expected, thank you."

"The comrades from the embassy will take us to our hotel after we collect your suitcase. There is a party still going on at the lobby bar in our hotel. Some of your teammates are probably waiting for you there."

Mejias asked Lince for his passport and ID card. For the third time in his life, he had been left without documentation in a foreign country.

The men retrieved Lince's bag from the luggage claim area and walked outside to board a black Mercedes 300 with diplomatic license plates parked by the curb. Lince noticed that the embassy guys had not shaken hands with him or made eye contact. He guessed the men were probably part of a DGI team assigned to watch him in Mexico and did not want him to become familiar with their faces.

It was close to midnight when the embassy operatives dropped off Mejias and Lince at the front door of the four-star hotel in the center of Mexico City. Mejias went straight to his room, while Lince walked up to the lobby bar where a dozen or so skydivers were still hanging out. Kymbe greeted him with a frosted bottle of Corona.

"Welcome to Mexico, Lince."

"Cheers, thank you. It has been an amazing odyssey, but here I am."

"Our room is on the first floor." Guerra said, handing him the key. "I'll be there in a few minutes."

Guerra had been one of Lince's teammates in both Hungary and Peru. But no longer qualified as a competitor, he had been sent to Mexico acting as the team trainer. Lince knew better. Guerra was part of the DSE security detail deployed to keep an eye on them.

Lince finished his beer and then headed to his room. His first impulse was to place the phone call to Duvalón, but decided against it. Guerra could show up at any moment.

The skydiver opened a nightstand drawer and pulled out a copy of Mexico City's phone book. He flipped quickly through the

white pages until he found the listing he was looking for—
Embajada de los Estados Unidos. He committed both the American
embassy address and phone number to memory and returned the
book to the drawer. It would be good to have a backup in case the
Duvalón plan did not work. Moments later, he heard a loud knock
on the door. It was Guerra.

It took the team's van nearly two hours to cover the sixty five
mile stretch that separated Mexico City from Tequesquitengo, the
site of the Pan American skydiving event. The fenced-in airfield
stood in a small semi-arid valley and next to a scenic lake. The
place was totally exposed, with very few houses, trees or other
structures standing nearby. It would be nearly impossible for
someone to walk in or out of the airfield without being noticed.

Two years earlier, in Collique, Lince had mulled over the idea
of escaping from the airfield. It would not be difficult for a skydiver
to exit a jump plane downwind of the target area during a
competition jump and land the parachute outside the airport's
perimeter. That plan, however, would require having a trusted
accomplice waiting in a getaway car. He never found anyone in
Peru whom he could commission with that task.

After a brief tour of the airfield, all the teams were taken to
their lodging resort in Oaxtepec located one-hour drive away. That
same night, Lince spotted Mejias talking to a man outside the
resort's main entrance. Both men were in the shadows, but Lince
was able to recognize the stranger; it was one of the two embassy
operatives who picked him up at the airport.

This could only mean one thing; the DGI had decided to deploy a surveillance detail in Oaxtepec. If that was the case, the embassy would have two teams there working on a rotating schedule. The operatives would take turns watching the airfield during the day, and the resort's perimeter at night for the duration of the event. That unexpected development made Lince discard any ideas of getting away from the airfield, or from the resort itself. He would have to wait until the team went to Mexico D.F., or to another major city before making his move.

A few days into the competition, the organizers announced a day of recess from the skydiving activities. Most of the competitors would be spending the day of leisure at the resort, or travel to the nearby tourist traps. The Cuban team had a busier schedule. They would travel to Mexico City and spend their day off shopping.

Shopping was always a highly anticipated activity for Cuban athletes competing abroad, and for a good reason. It gave them the opportunity to buy items that were either rationed or unavailable on the island, like shoes, clothes and watches. It was also the way the regime incentivized and rewarded them for their efforts and try to keep them loyal.

The unexpected trip to Mexico City was the break Lince had been waiting for. With a population of nearly seven million people, the huge metropolis could offer him a chance to disappear within its multitudes. He believed he could get lost in that big city with relative ease, the same way he got separated by accident from his teammates in Prague's Old Town Square back in 1974.

On the eve of the day off, the Mexican hosts invited all the participants to a party at the Oaxtepec resort. Lince thought this could be the perfect time to make contact with the captain of the U.S. Army team. There was a still slight chance that the State Department, through the Department of the Army had told Captain O'Donnell about his intentions. If that was the case, O'Donnell could have some fresh information for him.

Lince needed to find someone who could relay the message to O'Donnell. He could not risk to be seen talking to any of the Americans. There had to be someone at the party in whom he could trust with the delicate assignment.

By nine o'clock, the resort's inner courtyard was bustling with skydivers, coaches, and judges. Lince stepped down onto the Saltillo floor and grabbed a cold beer from one of the stalls. It took him a few seconds to spot a man he knew well standing alone next to an open fire pit. It was Severino Andrade, a member of the team from Uruguay.

He had met Severino, or Sam as most jumpers liked to call him, at the Pan American Games in Peru. Back then, Sam had introduced Lince to an old tradition of his country—sharing a *Mate* tea. The *Mate*, known in Uruguay as an *amargo*, was brewed by pouring hot water over *yerba mate* leaves inside a hollow calabash gourd. The steaming brew was then sipped slowly through a metal tube called *bombilla*. One memorable evening, the skydivers had sat in a circle by the bonfire to share a *Mate,* tell jokes, and enjoy the moon that shone brightly above the Valley of Collique.

Sam's waggish humor had made him very popular amongst the competitors. He spoke with a heavy Uruguayan accent and had a natural talent for making everyone in his audience double over with laughter. He was quite older and more mature than the rest. Sam could indeed be the perfect guy for the job.

"It's not like you to party alone," Lince said, placing a hand on his friend's shoulder.

Startled by Lince, Sam turned around and then smiled.

"Well, it's nice to see you. Where are your shadows tonight?"

"They are probably hiding not far from here. I wouldn't be surprised if one of them shows up unexpectedly. They just have to see me chatting with someone from another team to come running to my rescue."

Sam chuckled. "I'll probably make it on Fidel's hit list tonight."

"Sam, I need a favor from you. I hate to put you in an awkward position, but I don't have many choices. Can I trust you with something extremely delicate and confidential?"

Sam gave Lince a puzzled look. "I'll be obliged. Which of the girls do you want to meet tonight?"

"This is not about ladies. It's a very serious matter—serious enough that if the Cubans find out it could cost me my life."

"Now you got me excited, but very worried. Yes, of course you can trust me. What is it?"

"Sam, I'm not going back to Cuba. I need you to find Fred O'Donnell, the captain of the Golden Knights, and give him a message on my behalf."

"Okay, but please let me catch my breath first. What do you want me to tell O'Donnell?"

"Tell Fred that I had to relay the message through you because I cannot be seen talking to him. Tell him that my father is an American citizen and that I want to defect to the United States. My only chance to get away will be tomorrow when we go to Mexico City."

"I had no idea about your feelings, although something like this can be expected from people from communist countries. Thank you for your trust. I will do what you asked of me, and promise to remain tight-lipped until you are a free man."

"Thank you, Sam. I'll be waiting right here for you."

Sam walked away nonchalantly and soon disappeared in the crowds. Five minutes later, the Uruguayan was back at the fire pit looking agitated.

"Nick, I just gave your message to Captain O'Donnell. He made me swear on the flag of my country that I was telling the truth. Then he told me that you must cross the golden gates as soon as you can. That's all he said."

"Thanks again, Sam. I could never repay you for the favor. You are a good man."

"May God be with you at all times. I'll be praying that all goes well tomorrow. Just make sure to tie your shoelaces well in case you have to run fast." Both men erupted in a nervous laughter.

O'Donnell had relayed back to Lince a metaphor that could be interpreted in many different ways. *Tell him to cross the golden gates*, were O'Donnell's words. Sam wasn't fluent in English and something crucial might have been lost in the translation. Had the American captain meant for Lince to go straight to the American Embassy? Or was it something totally different? He would have to analyze those words carefully during the team's drive to the city.

Lince's first impulse upon arriving at the resort had been to place the call to Duvalón. But the only pay phone he could find stood next to the reception desk. He could not take the risk of having someone from his team spot him talking on the phone. The call to Duvalón would have to wait until a later time.

The next morning, Mejias rounded up the team as the skydivers started to trickle into the resort's breakfast room.

"There has been a slight change of plans. We have been invited to visit the Cuban Embassy in Mexico City before our shopping spree today."

Mejias handed each team member an envelope with their money allowance. Lince counted the cash and did the math. He had the equivalent of two hundred and fifty American dollars in Mexican currency. That should be enough to pay for a taxi ride if he ever needed to travel to a distant place in Mexico.

The skydiver helped him to a stack of pancakes and scrambled eggs at the buffet bar, and then joined his teammates at a table. The Golden Knights had put several tables together and were having their breakfast only a few feet away from the Cubans.

Lince's eyes met briefly with Fred O'Donnell's, long enough to notice a spark of encouragement in the man's gaze. He looked around the restaurant for Sam, but his friend was nowhere to be found.

Chapter 31

The sign on the narrow, one way street reads *Campos Eliseos* and nothing else. It does not indicate whether it is a street, an avenue, or lane. Shortly after steering the van into the alley the driver made a sharp turn and halted in front of a massive stone wall with an iron gate. They had reached the back entrance of the Cuban Embassy in Mexico City. The Cubans had indeed built a seemingly impregnable fortress smack in the heart of Mexico City.

The driver rolled down his window and spoke to the guard inside the concrete gatehouse by way of an intercom. Seconds later, the electrically operated gate opened to allow the van inside, then closed behind them with a loud thump. Technically speaking, the skydiving team was back on Cuban soil.

Although trips to the embassy were not unusual for Cuban delegations visiting Mexico, the skydiver worried about the last minute change of plans. Had someone from his group, or from the surveillance team deployed in Oaxtepec watched him talking to Sam the night before? If that was the case, they already had him.

While everyone in the group had brought along their team handbags to use them for shopping, Lince had taken his' for a totally different reason. Hidden under a newspaper at the bottom of his bag was his skydiving logbook and his competitor's ID badge—the only two items he intended to take with him to his new life in freedom.

The delegation was greeted at the embassy's door by a man who introduced himself as Lopez. Lopez asked them to leave their handbags and coats in the foyer, then ushered the group through several inner hallways. At the end of one corridor, the man stepped aside to let everyone into a room packed with radio communications equipment.

The lone occupant of that room was a gray-haired man in his early sixties seated in front of a sophisticated radio set. The man wore thick reading glasses and had a set of aviator's headphones clamped over his ears.

"Comrades, Commander Enrique Carreras has been waiting eagerly to meet all of you," Lopez said.

Nearly everyone in Cuba had heard of Enrique Carreras, a former Sea Fury pilot who flew sorties for Castro's Air Force during the Bay of Pigs invasion. Flying in unchallenged skies, Carreras got credit for sinking several ships from the 2506 Brigade and for strafing the troops wading waist-deep in the swamps. For those actions, the Cuban regime had made Carreras a national hero.

Operating under the cover of Cuban Military Attaché in Mexico, the butcher of Bay of Pigs was now in charge of the Department Americas Command and Control center in Mexico City. The DA was responsible for all Cuban subversive activities south of the Rio Grande, and for random missions in the United States.

When Lince shook hands with Carreras, it crossed his mind

that the man standing in front of him owed his life to former U.S. president John Fitzgerald Kennedy. Carreras may not have lived totell the story had the A4D-2 Skyhawk pilots flown their planned sorties in support of the exiled Cuban forces. Luckily for the Sea Fury pilot, the White House withdrew at the last moment the air umbrella it had pledged in support of the invasion.

"Welcome, skydivers. I must admit I have a great respect for all of you. But I still think that you must be crazy. The only time I would have thought of using a parachute was if my airplane had caught fire, or lost a wing."

"You should know that the commander-in-chief is following your progress at the Pan American Games very closely. That alone makes your role here twice as important. Nothing would bring Fidel more satisfaction than a victory against the Yankees."

The team's impromptu encounter with the former Cuban pilot lasted less than ten minutes. Lopez guided the bulk of the group back to the lobby, while Mejias, Guerra and Urbano stayed behind in the military attaché's office.

From his chair in the embassy's lobby, Lince could see his handbag still leaning against the foyer wall in the same spot where he had left it. He hoped it had not been searched while they were at the meeting with Carreras. He would find it difficult to explain why he had brought his skydiving log book to the shopping spree.

Lince grew more paranoid as the minutes passed. The supposedly brief visit to the embassy had already consumed a good part of an hour, and there was still no sign of Mejias, Guerra, or Urbano.

Meanwhile, Pablo and Lauris were called into the offices separately for about twenty minutes each, but neither man offered an explanation for their private meetings with the embassy officials. Lince feared that his teammates had been debriefed by the DGI, specifically about his movements in the past few days. He thought of Mendez back in Havana, holding the proverbial *Sword of Damocles* over his head. Had the intelligence colonel received conclusive evidence that he had struck a deal with the Americans?

Lince thought he might never see another sunrise again. If things had gone sour, the DGI agents stationed in Mexico could put him in shackles, inject him with a heavy sedative and spirit him back to Havana on the next Cubana flight out of Mexico. Mejias would tell the organizers at the Pan American competition that Lince had fallen ill during their trip to the city and was left behind under the care of the Cuban ambassador.

The moment the team's van pulled out of the embassy compound, Lince realized he didn't have much time to make his move.

The commander-in-chief is following your progress at the Pan American Games very closely, Carreras had told them.

Chapter 32

The Lord is faithful, and he will strengthen you.
— *Thessalonians 3:4*

A wayward gust of wind lifted a cluster of *Ocozol* leaves from the curb and made them dance momentarily in mid air, then scattered them on the broad sidewalk. It was a brisk ten degrees Celsius in Mexico City.

Lince flipped up his coat collar and turned his back to the cool wind while he and his teammates waited for Mejias to give last minute instructions to the driver. The pickup would be at four o'clock sharp at that same spot. Mejias assured the group that would be enough time to do their shopping, and then make it back to the resort in time to attend the event's official banquet that evening.

"Lopez suggested a shopping center half a mile from here. We need to stay close together. Everyone knows the drill."

A quick glance at his watch told Lince they had hardly one hour and thirty minutes left to shop. In spite of Mejias' assurance, that was very little time indeed considering the stores were still a long ways away. He had to find a way to make their tight schedule work to his advantage.

The moment the group stepped out of the van, Lince noticed Pablo getting too close for comfort. The unusual behavior suggested the embassy officials might have ordered his teammate to shadow him during the shopping spree. Pablo would be a logical choice for the task. He was on active duty with the air force parachute team and a raucous member of the Communist Youth. He was also a few inches taller than Lince and in excellent physical shape. Lince would need a significant head start if he wanted to outrun Pablo in the streets of Mexico City.

At Mejias' command, the group started down the broad sidewalk toward the shopping district. Lince put on his Ray Ban sunglasses and went on to scout every side street and alley for a potential escape route. It was near rush hour in Mexico City and the sidewalk was getting congested by the minute. Still, it wasn't crowded enough for him to be able to peel off from the group unnoticed. With twelve people in his entourage, any of them could spot him if he started heading in a different direction. Also, he could not discard the possibility that the DGI had dispatched one or more agents to shadow the group from a distance.

A store ahead with a sign that advertised reading glasses for sale gave him an idea. He slowed down his pace and halted in front of the store's window display.

As he had anticipated, it took Pablo just a couple of seconds to turn around and rush to his side. His teammate then uttered a loud whistle to warn the rest of the group. Everyone stopped on their tracks and walked back to the place where Pablo and Lince stood.

"What's the matter guys?" Mejias asked them.

"I'm sorry to hold up the group, but I promised my father a pair of reading glasses."

"Do you need to buy them in this particular store?"

"They have a sale going on. It will only take me a few minutes."

Lince pretended to search in his jean pocket, ripped the seam he had sewn at the bottom and pulled out the small piece of paper with Duvalón's phone number written in code.

"*Voilà*, I found the prescription."

Lince folded the paper again and returned it to his pocket. He had trusted the prescription to memory, but pretending he had brought it along gave him a more convincing argument.

He felt Pablo virtually breathing down his neck as he chose an imitation turtle shell frame from a display and gave the store clerk the prescription for the lenses. Minutes later, the skydiver walked out of the drugstore with a new pair of reading glasses that his father would never get to wear. But most importantly, he had confirmed the identity of his secret bodyguard. He could not lose sight of Pablo.

The brief stop to buy his father's glasses had consumed valuable minutes from the team's tight schedule. He could sense that everyone in the group was getting impatient, mindful of the little time they had left to do their own shopping. Once the frenzy started, he expected all of them to become absorbed by their own agendas and relax their watch over him.

Mejias eventually waved the group to a stop in front of two large department stores. The one on the left sold children's clothing. To their right stood a general apparel store with blue jeans, polo shirts, shoes and other garments on display in the front windows.

"Those of us with kids can start here," Mejias said, pointing at the store on the left.

"I'm going next door," Pablo said. "Who's coming with me?"

Almost in unison, Kymbe, Lauris, Raul, and Lince raised their hands indicating that they would follow Pablo.

"Great. Let's meet out here in half an hour," Mejias said.

Lince stood still on the sidewalk for a few seconds to make sure he was the last person to follow Pablo inside. He glanced up the street and estimated the distance to the next corner to be about forty yards. It was a busy crossroad where two eight-lane avenues intersected. At the end of the sidewalk was a large circular kiosk that sold newspapers, magazines and postcards. The entire area was getting crowded by the second with pedestrians walking in all directions. It was the start of rush hour in Mexico City.

He followed Pablo and the other three in the store keeping a reasonable distance from them. Pablo turned around to look at him for a second, but then kept on going.

At that point, Lince had his four teammates in his field of vision. The men looked mesmerized as they sifted earnestly through the racks of shirts and blue jeans that crammed the establishment.

He lost sight of Lauris and Raul momentarily, but assumed they could not see him either. Slowly, he retraced his steps backwards toward the entrance pretending that something in the front window had caught his attention. He had been inside less than five or six seconds.

It was time to go. He figured that once Pablo discovered he was missing, his first thought might be he had gone next door to the second group. That initial confusion should buy him the precious seconds he needed to walk away from the store and reach the kiosk—his most immediate target.

Lince stepped onto the sidewalk and started walking towards the corner. He kept a casual stride at first, keeping as close to the building walls as possible. He felt like he was in the middle of a bad dream, wading in knee-high water against an invisible current that hindered his advance. He had reached the point of no return.

"Traveler, there is no path-you make the path as you walk on. And in looking back one sees the trodden road that never will be set foot on again."

The verses of an old poem by Antonio Machado came to mind as Lince headed resolutely toward the unknown. Half the way to the intersection, the skydiver hastened his stride. His heart was now beating out of control in his chest. All of the sudden, he thought he heard someone calling his name. Had he been spotted by one of his teammates? Or maybe by an asset from the Cuban Embassy?

Keep on going, but don't run yet, he thought to himself. *And don't look back. If you do, someone could recognize your face. Then they'll know for sure it's you.*

"Traveler, there is no path-you make the path as you walk on. But don't dare to look back"

The kiosk was only ten yards away, five yards...now!

The skydiver started to run and nearly fell as he tripped over a pile of newspapers stacked against the round stand.

"Perdón amigo. I'm sorry," he yelled at the startled vendor. Lince needed to make it quickly to the other side of the boulevard and widen the gap between him and his impending pursuers. He stepped onto the pavement and started to cross the street, dodging the traffic that was

already slowing down for the red light ahead. That was when he spotted the vacant taxi some twenty yards away and heading in his direction.

The cab driver didn't have a chance to react. All he saw from the corner of his eye was a young man in a brown overcoat and dark sunglasses appearing out of nowhere. The stranger darted straight for his cab like the devil himself was after him, opened the back door and dove head first into the vehicle.

"Take me away from here as fast as possible, *rápido*."

"*A dónde desea ir señor*—where to?"

"I don't know yet, just drive. And please don't turn the fare meter on. I promise to pay you generously."

Lince wanted the cabbie to keep the vacant sign lit to confuse whoever might be on his tail. An unoccupied cab with the light on should not draw attention if someone were trying to find him in the passing vehicles. He had to stay down and out of sight.

While lying flat on the cab's floor, Lince said a prayer for his mother and father back in Cuba. He had not prayed in more than eighteen years, but the words poured from his heart with unexpected ease. He sensed that God was actually listening that time around.

The taxi's wheels rolled forward for a few feet and then halted again, waiting for the traffic light to turn green. He could not remember ever being so aware of an impending threat, or having so many reasons to stay alive. Lince have had many close calls skydiving, but this was by far the most extreme experience ever in his life. He'd been longing for this very moment for eighteen years.

Lince waited a good minute before sitting up to look out the window. A quick glance through the back windshield confirmed they had not been followed. Now he had to find a pay phone and make the call to Duvalón, the enigmatic stranger whom he expected will give him shelter and eventually help him get out of Mexico.

The cab driver, a small man in his late sixties, kept looking at him on and off through the rear view mirror—probably trying to guess what kind of trouble the man had gotten into. The old driver would never realize drama he had just played an accidental part in, or that his passenger's odyssey was far from over. Soon, there will be some very bad people looking all over Mexico City for the guy in the back seat.

"Where to?" asked the driver for the second time.

"I don't know yet. First, please take me to a pay phone, but not around here. Keep on driving for a few more blocks and then turn onto a side street."

"No problem, *señor*."

Lince started to wonder what the man known as Duvalón looked like.

THE LYNX

Chapter 33

Pablo was busy sorting through a rack of blue jeans when he realized he had not checked up on his teammate for a while. He turned around to look for him and then panicked when he could not find him.

He located Kymbe, Lauris, and Raul right away, but there was no sign of the one person he wanted so badly to be there. Pablo rounded up the guys.

"Have any of you seen Lince?"

It was of no use. Nobody remembered the last time they saw their teammate.

Pablo thought there was still a chance the man had joined the group next door. Lince wasn't married and didn't have children, but perhaps decided to go and buy something for the child of a relative, or a friend. He asked the guys to keep searching in that store while he ran outside and checked with the other group. Mejias and the others were all there, but there was no trace of Lince.

"Something happened to him," Pablo stammered. "We've got

to keep on searching."

In spite of his wishful thinking, Pablo had a feeling that Lince would not be found. The ever-dreaded vanishing act of a Cuban athlete during a competition abroad had happened once again. Unfortunately, there was nothing that he or anyone else could do to change the outcome.

The phone rang twice before the small man with the thick-rimmed glasses picked-up the handset.

"General Carreras here."

"I have Mejias from the skydiving delegation on the line. He said it's urgent."

"Put him on."

"General. I have bad news. One of our skydivers is gone, vanished."

"Who is he? Where and when did this happen?"

"It's Nickolich, the one they call Lince. It happened fifteen, maybe twenty minutes ago. He went missing while our group was shopping in a department store."

"Did anyone see him getting away?"

"Nobody did. We had been in the stores less than five or ten minutes when Pablo noticed he was gone. We spent another five minutes searching that store and the immediate area."

"Stand by and keep all your people together. I will send a van for you. Where are you exactly?"

The military attaché wrote down the name of the store and hung up the phone. He picked it up again and dialed Alcides

Sanchez' office to give him the news and the coordinates where Mejias and his group stood waiting. Alcides was the DGI station chief in Mexico.

Commander Carreras glanced at his Rolex GMT, an expensive timepiece presented to him by Fidel at a ceremony in the Palace of the Revolution. Fidel, who felt indebted to Carreras for his decisive role during the Bay of Pigs invasion, had rewarded the pilot with his signature gift. In the sixties and beyond, Rolex GMT and Rolex Submariner watches were the most recognized symbols of power and status in Cuba.

"What a bunch of idiots," Carreras cried out loud. "Twenty minutes! The guy could be anywhere by now. Wait till they hear the news in La Habana!"

The military attaché took a stack of passports from a desk drawer and singled-out one in particular. With Lince's passport in hand, Carreras ran over to Alcides' office. He found Lopez and another DGI agent already waiting there. Carreras handed the passport to Lopez.

"Make several enlargements of his picture and get every available car ready to roll out."

"On my way Comandante."

Alcides took off his reading glasses and looked at Carreras in the eye.

"It's of no use to point fingers now, but Colonel Mendez should have never allowed this guy to leave Cuba. Let's hope we can find him before it's too late."

"It was not Mendez' fault alone. Too many people wanted the team's victory to happen. We are also to blame, Alcides. There was enough circumstantial evidence this morning to keep the guy detained here and then sent back to Cuba. We let him go instead."

"Like they say, hindsight is twenty/twenty."

"By the way, do you know why they call this guy *el Lince*?"

Alcides chuckled. "Commander, I know this is not funny, but I think Nick is living up to his nickname. The Lynx, as you know, is a very elusive and fast cat."

Carreras seemed flustered at Alcides' remark. "I figured that much myself. Get in touch with the Mexican minister of foreign affairs. Give him his physical description. Twenty-six years old, medium-tall with brown hair, hazel eyes and a mustache. He is wearing blue jeans and a brown overcoat. The police needs to be made aware that he is dangerous and should be taken into custody without delay."

Alcides pulled a street map of Mexico City from a drawer and unfolded it on top of his desk. Using a pencil, he drew a large circle on the map around the area where the department store was located.

"We need to watch the area where he was last seen. He could still be hiding in the vicinity of the store."

"Send out as many people as you need. We need to either capture him, or take him out," Carreras said as he stormed out of the office.

The DGI station chief in Mexico glanced at the three black telephone sets lined up on top of his desk. Deep in his heart, he hoped that one of them would start ringing soon. Secured with Scotch tape to the handset of the middle phone was a small piece of paper with a name written on it—*Duvalón*.

Colonel Mendez had told him that Duvalón could be their ace in the hole if something went wrong.

It was *Murphy's Law*. Alcides had read somewhere that the Americans used that cliché whenever anything that could go wrong indeed went wrong.

Within thirty minutes of Lince's escape, six men carrying custom-made attaché cases rushed out of the Cuban Embassy building and stepped into three black Mercedes Benz 300s. The cars rolled swiftly through the rear embassy gate and then sped away in different directions. In each of the attaché cases was an enlarged copy of the fugitive's passport picture, a fully loaded AK-47 automatic rifle with a folding stock and a spare thirty-round magazine.

The first Mercedes headed straight for the American Embassy located only minutes away. Nick was the son of an American citizen and the U.S. embassy would be a logical place for him to go. The second car would go and park near the area where Lince had made his escape. The man could be hiding somewhere around there waiting for the right moment to surface and run. If that were the case, Alcides' agents would be ready to grab him.

The men in the third Mercedes were instructed to recon the embassy of Uruguay. Alcides had not overlooked the possibility that the Uruguayan man observed talking to Nick the night before might have asked his embassy to give political asylum to the Cuban skydiver.

All the DGI agents dispatched on the assignment had received the exact same orders-bring the man called Lince back to the embassy, dead or alive.

Alcides picked up one of the phones on his desk and asked the embassy's operator to connect him with the Mexican Foreign

Ministry. Within minutes, he had the assistant to the minister on the line and proceeded to follow to a tee the orders given to him by Commander Carreras.

Lastly, the DGI station chief placed a call to a personal friend in the Mexican Federal Directorate of Security. The DFS guys would be the first ones to know the minute Lince showed up his face anywhere in Mexico City.

The hunt for the Lynx had begun.

Chapter 34

The taxi was about one mile from the intersection where Lince had boarded it when the skydiver had a sudden change of heart. Perhaps calling Duvalón wasn't such a good idea after all. Something wasn't right. While the message the American gave him over the phone back in Cuba seemed legitimate, the mode of delivery made him suspect foul play.

A thousand thoughts were now racing through his mind at the speed of light. It didn't make sense for the State Department, or other U.S. government agency to send an operative into Cuba just to give him information to facilitate his defection. The risks involved were too big, both for the agent and for himself. If the U.S. government wanted to help in any way, they could have waited until he arrived in Mexico to contact him. Someone could have secretly handed him a note at the competition site, or at the lodging resort in Oaxtepec.

There were many ways the Cuban intelligence could have found out about his intentions. A number of U.S. State Department employees had been residing and working in Havana for the last eight weeks, while an equal number of Cuban envoys had settled in Washington, D.C. Lince had a gut feeling that someone had double-crossed him.

He quickly concluded the DGI must have set him up. The man who called his house acting as an American agent had to be a trained operative with the Cuban intelligence. The Cubans probably had many assets at hand who spoke native English. Over time, the intelligence agency could have recruited some of the fugitives from U.S. justice who lived on the island under the protection of the Cuban government.

If he were right, the phone number the alleged American gave him over the phone would ring instead inside the Cuban Embassy in Mexico, or at one of their offices in the city. The person answering the phone would provide him with an address. If he unwisely went to that address, armed agents from the Cuban Embassy could be waiting to grab him and take him away. It was time for plan B.

"There is a pay phone less than a block ahead," the cabbie said.

"*Amigo*, forget about the pay phone. Take me to the American Embassy instead, Paseo de la Reforma 305, *pronto*."

"No problem, *señor*. I know where that is."

"How long before we get there?"

"It's rush hour and the traffic will be heavy on Reforma. I think I can get you there in about twenty minutes."

"Make it in fifteen and I'll triple your fare."

After what seemed like an eternity, the driver looked back at Lince again through the rearview mirror.

"We are almost there. Up ahead is the Angel of Independence circle. The American Embassy is on the other side of that circle."

As the taxi approached the roundabout, Lince got a clear view of an impressive monument dating back to the turn of the century. It was an elaborate obelisk supporting a huge gold-plated sculpture of an angel with its wings spread open. The angel held a laurel wreath up high in one hand and a broken chain in the other.

Those broken chains must be a good omen, he thought.

Lince leaned against the taxi's front seat, looking for the embassy beyond the row of trees that lined the boulevard. The driver brought the vehicle to a halt about one hundred feet beyond the roundabout and then stretched his arm straight out the window. He was pointing at a building on the opposite side of Paseo de la Reforma.

"*Ahí está*—there she is."

The skydiver's heart skipped a beat. Out in plain view was a modern building with the stars-and-stripes flag waving gently on top of a pole. He also noticed that the embassy grounds were protected on all sides by a tall, wrought-iron fence.

Lince took out the equivalent of one hundred dollars in Mexican pesos from his wallet and handed it to the taxi driver. The man's eyes opened wide at the sight of the money.

"That's a lot of money, sir. Thank you very much and God bless you."

"Enjoy it and God bless you too, my friend. You just saved my life."

The skydiver stepped out of the taxi and took off sprinting across the eight lanes of Paséo de la Reforma, zigzagging his way through the fast-moving traffic. He still had two serious obstacles ahead of him. One was the tall iron fence—the other were two Mexican police officers pacing on the sidewalk.

Don't think about it, just do it, Lince thought. *Make it over the fence before the cops get to you, or shoot you.*

As he ran between the moving cars, Lince noticed a small pedestrian gate a few feet from where the policemen stood. *The gate was open.* Had Fred O'Donnell called the embassy and warned them of his impending arrival? Could that be the Golden Gate that Fred mentioned to Sam the night before?

Lince likened his tunnel-vision approach to the gate to landing his parachute in a tight spot. Once committed, he had to go for it regardless. There would be no room for error.

The two officers from the Mexican police didn't see Lince until he was only a few feet away. One of them reacted by trying to block the gate with his body, but the runner was carrying a powerful momentum. It would take a brick wall to stop him now.

"*Soy Americano*—I'm an American," he yelled as he pushed the officer broadside against the fence and soared into the embassy grounds.

In a twinkle of a star, Lince crossed the deep abyss that separated bondage from freedom.

The skydiver did not stop, or even looked back. He kept on running until he reached the wide steps leading to the embassy building. On top of the stairs, he saw a young U.S. Marine in dress uniform watching him impassively at perfect attention.

The marine had first noticed the man running from the opposite side of the boulevard. Seconds later, he saw him push aside one of the Mexican guards and rush to the embassy grounds through the gate. As the stranger was about to take his first step up the stairs, the embassy guard raised his hand and gestured him to stop.

Moments later, the young Marine would be the first person to learn it had taken the runner eighteen years to cross the finish line.

Lince's ordeal, however, was not yet over.

"I would like to make an important appeal to the American ambassador," Lince told the two men debriefing him from the other side of the glossy conference table. They had introduced themselves as Morris and Thomas—probably agents with the FBI, or the CIA, or both.

"We are listening."

"I need to have someone from the U.S. Special interest mission in Cuba visit my parents at their home as soon as possible. My father is an American citizen and my defection today has put both him and my mother in grave danger."

"Your concern has been noted. The ambassador will be advised at the first possible opportunity."

"Thank you."

"Why did your family stay in Cuba after the first exodus wave in the early sixties?" Thomas asked.

"It was my father's decision, and one that unfortunately proved to be the worst mistake of his life. He had just turned sixty-four and thought he was too old to start over elsewhere. Like many others, he never thought Castro would last long in power. My mother, on the other hand, wanted us to pack our bags and leave the same day Castro's forces marched into Havana."

"You told us that your sister left for the United States ten years ago. How did she get out?"

"She left Cuba via Mexico and was issued an American passport at this same embassy. By then, my father realized he should have taken the whole family out a long time ago. But it was too late for us. I had turned of military age and the regime would not allow me to leave. My parents could have left for the United States by themselves, but they would have never abandoned me in Cuba. Our family's last hope was for me to escape first and then my parents would follow."

"It took guts to do what you did. We'll make sure that our people in Havana go and visit your folks soon."

Lince took a sip of water and glanced at a portrait on the wall across the table. It was the picture of a smiling gentleman in a suit and tie standing next to the American flag. The man had a kind face and bright blue eyes that seemed to be looking straight at Lince. His name was Jimmy Carter, the thirty-ninth President of the United States. However, it was not the man itself, but the stars and stripes flag by which he stood that reassured Lince he was indeed in safe hands.

"Should we order pizza?" Thomas asked him.

"Anything will do, thank you."

Lince was starving and very tired. His odyssey in the streets of Mexico City had taken a toll on his endurance. The debriefing by Morris and Thomas had been a long and tedious endeavor. At times, he noticed his answers flowing seamlessly out of his mouth. Others, he thought he didn't make any sense at all.

It had been a monumental task to try to summarize his lifelong journey in just a few hours using names, dates and places. Which part of his life was significant to the Americans, and which would be deemed irrelevant? Without unscrambling the entire picture, it would be impossible for anyone to understand why the Cuban intelligence had suspected him of treason only a few days earlier and yet still sent him to compete in Mexico.

Lince gave a detailed account of everything that transpired in the months and weeks before his departure from Havana. He told them about the visit by the Canadians to Cuba and his plea for help to the U.S. State Department through Henry Kissinger's aide and, of course, about his suspicions that someone had betrayed him.

He wondered if the message he had sent to Kissinger had reached the American Embassy in Mexico, or if Captain O'Donnell had contacted the Embassy that morning. Morris and Thomas, however, didn't volunteer anything that revealed any prior knowledge of his possible arrival. They just asked questions and took notes on their yellow pads.

At his office in a different floor of the embassy, Ambassador Patrick Lucey had been exchanging encrypted telexes with Cyrus Vance, the U.S. Secretary of State. A Cuban defector had shown up at the American Embassy steps with assassins following on his heels. The man claimed to be the son of an American citizen and had asked for political protection. It did not take long for the State Department to verify the defector's identity and confirm that he had close relatives residing in the United States.

Vance seemed unsure on what to do next. It was difficult to tell how this unexpected crisis would play out in the light of the ongoing negotiations between the U.S. and Cuba. At Vance's request, Lucey placed an urgent call to Alfonso Rosenzweig Diaz, Mexico undersecretary of Foreign Affairs. He asked the undersecretary to grant the skydiver political asylum in Mexico. At first, Rosenzweig Diaz rejected Lucey's request. He pointed out that such action would create an embarrassing situation between Cuba and Mexico on the eve of Foreign Secretary Santiago Roel's visit to Cuba.[13] Roel was scheduled to leave for a meeting with Fidel Castro in Havana within the next few days.

As an alternative solution, Rosenzweig Diaz suggested to Lucey that he could grant the defector temporary refugee status at the American Embassy, or arrange for his immediate passage to the United States. Lucey replied that the embassy did not have the proper facilities, or a place where to keep the defector safe from being kidnapped by Cuban agents before being spirited to the United States.

Ambassador Lucey insisted that the Mexican government should take charge of the man and keep him at a safe location until Roel's visit to Cuba was over. Rosenzweig Diaz said that he doubted he could get such action approved.

Pressured by Lucey, Rosenzweig Diaz eventually ceded. Nick would be granted protection by the Mexican Secret Service and housed at a safe location in Mexico City pending a U.S. decision to authorize his entry into the United States. He urged the ambassador to make that decision a top priority.

"Secretary Vance would like full assurance that Nick would not be turned over to the Cuban authorities."

"Rest assured that we will not hand him over to the Cubans," Rosenzweig replied.

"Furthermore, we would like for the Mexican government to take full measures to protect the skydiver from a possible kidnap

---

[13] Page 346

attempt by the Cubans while he's in your custody."

"I can guarantee you that your man will be under a round-the-clock protection by agents from the Federal Directorate of Security."

In a wire sent to Cyrus Vance that same day, Ambassador Lucey requested the immediate pre parole of Nick into the United States. He stressed that the United States should cooperate in relieving Mexico of an embarrassing situation that a failure to act would otherwise create.

After hanging up the phone with the American ambassador, Undersecretary Rosenzweig Diaz summoned the head of the FDS, the Federal Directorate of Security, and instructed him to handle this situation personally and only with his most trusted men.

"One more thing, Commander Vasquez. Please make sure there are no secret admirers of Fidel in Nick's security detail."

After being gone for a good half hour, Morris entered the room again for the twentieth time or so. Nick glanced at his watch and noticed it was past midnight.

"Nick, the State Department and Ambassador Lucey have decided that you need to be taken to a safe place. Unfortunately, our embassy does not have a safe house in Mexico City that would serve that purpose."

"I see." Morris paused to take a sip from his water glass.

"At Ambassador's Lucey's request, the government of Mexico has agreed to grant you a temporary political asylum status until we can bring you into the United States. It's just a formality to guarantee your personal safety while you are in this country. A Mexican Secret Service detail will be in charge of your personal protection until you receive the green light to leave Mexico."

"That will be a big mistake," Lince protested. "Mexico has handed over many Cuban defectors to Castro over the years."

"You of all people should know that Mexico and Cuba are the closest of allies, and that the authorities here will go to great lengths to keep it that way," he added.

Morris chuckled. "Nick, you have nothing to worry about. The U.S. State Department and the Mexican Foreign Service have given your personal safety a top priority. The foreign secretary has given the State Department full guarantees that the Cuban agents will not get anywhere near you. The people in your security detail are the same guys who protect the Mexican president. They are some of the best in their field."

"The FDS guys will be here in twenty minutes. By the way, Ambassador Lucey wants you to know he had sent a memo to the chief of the U.S. Interest Mission in Havana to visit your parents at the earliest possible time," Thomas said.

"That makes me feel a lot better. You guys have been very accommodating."

"No problem, we are just doing our job. Do you care for another slice of pizza?"

Chapter 35

At fifteen minutes past one in the morning, special agents Morris and Thomas told Lince it was time to go. The skydiver was escorted through a labyrinth of hallways on the first floor of the American Embassy. At the end of one corridor, Morris opened a small door and started down a narrow stairway leading to the embassy's underground garage. They found three men in trench coats already waiting on the floor, the tallest of them holding an Israeli UZI submachine gun in the open. A portly short man with a thick mustache took a step forward to shake hands with Lince.

"Mr. Nickolich, I'm Commander Vasquez from Mexico's Federal Directorate of Security. It's a pleasure to meet you. My two colleagues here, Sergio and Manuel, will be your personal bodyguards from now until the moment you leave for the United States."

"While in our custody, and for your own safety, you must do exactly as you are told. Our first stop tonight will be at the Secretariat of Interior's offices. A government official will be waiting there for us to complete certain formalities."

Lince thanked both Morris and Thomas. The men wished him good luck and reassured him that everything was going to be fine.

Meanwhile, Sergio had already opened the white VW van sliding door and asked the skydiver to step inside. Vasquez, who had gotten in the driver's seat of a dark green VW Beetle, took the lead.

Within seconds, the two-vehicle motorcade sped away from the American Embassy's garage and into Mexico City's night.

"Hold on tight, Nick," Sergio told him.

The ride to the Secretary of Interior's office was a harrowing experience even for a thrill-seeker like Lince. He likened the experience to getting a shot of pure adrenaline in his vein. The FDS vehicles went on a wild race through the nearly empty streets. They swapped the lead every few blocks, ran every red light they encountered, skid their tires on tight street corners and roundabouts, and made sudden turns in and out of narrow alleys. Lince had no doubt the men in charge of his protection had been trained well in the art of vehicular evasion tactics.

"No worries, Nick. We need to make sure that your Cuban friends are not on our tail. Earlier on, our people sighted several assets from the DGI watching the American Embassy."

The Secret Service motorcade slowed down as they approached a large colonial-style building near the center of the old city. Lince noticed a rolling gate opening as the van turned into the drive. Commander Vasquez, who was now following close behind, must have radioed in and advised the guard of their impending arrival. The vehicles zipped through a vaulted tunnel that cut under the building, emerging seconds later at a high-walled inner courtyard. It was one-forty five in the morning.

Lince followed Sergio and Manuel out of the van and joined Commander Vasquez in the cobblestone patio. The commander took a key from his pocket, unlocked a small wooden door and gestured the men to follow him inside. The hollow sound of four pairs of shoes resonated loudly as the men advanced rapidly through a long vaulted corridor. Vasquez opened another door and ushered the men into a sumptuous office. The room had bright marble floors and was lavishly furnished with Persian rugs and leather armchairs. Rich bookshelves made from the finest cedar wood lined the walls from floor to ceiling.

Waiting at a mahogany desk in the middle of the room was a lanky man in his late sixties. The light from a green-shade desk lamp on the desk gave his face a rather ghostly appearance. He had probably been awakened in the middle of the night to take care of the unexpected situation.

"Good evening, gentlemen. I'm Deputy Secretary Andrade. Please have a seat." Vasquez sat next to Lince, Sergio and Manuel stood behind them.

"Is everything in order?" Vasquez asked the man.

"Yes. I just need to ask Mr. Nickolich some routine questions and have him sign the request for asylum. It shouldn't take long."

The Mexican official placed a sheet of stationery in an Olivetti typewriter and started typing away. He asked Lince for his name, date of birth, country of origin, and the details of his evasion. He pulled the paper out of the machine and read it out loud.

"Mr. Nickolich, you were in Mexico attending an international parachuting competition? Is that correct?"

"Yes, sir."

"And on the afternoon of December 1st, 1977 you escaped from your team during a shopping spree in the district of Polanco?"

"Yes."

"And because of that action you now fear reprisals from the Cuban government?"

"I do."

"Do you wish to proceed with your request for political asylum from the Mexican government?"

"Yes."

The man handed him the document, and a fountain pen.

"Please double check that the information on this paper is correct. If it is, and you agree with what it says, then please sign your name at the bottom of the page."

Lince read the document in silence as the men from the Secret Service looked on. The deal offered to him by the secretary was not exactly what he had expected. If he signed the paper, he could be forced to stay in Mexico indefinitely. While in Mexican territory, he would be at risk of being kidnapped by Cuban agents. Castro had many friends in high places in that country, the kind of people who would not hesitate to give the Cuban government information on his whereabouts. However, the choice was no longer his.

Halfheartedly, he placed his signature on the document and handed it back to the secretary. The Mexican official then asked him to raise his right hand and swear that the information on the paper he just signed was the truth.

"I would like to thank the Mexican government for its kind hospitality, but also want to make it clear that I do not wish to stay in Mexico." He had chosen his words carefully as not to sound impolite.

"Your request for asylum in Mexico is only a formality. It's the only way our government can legally provide you with protection by the Secret Service agents who brought you here."

"However, it is the responsibility of the American government to secure your prompt passage to the United States."

"I understand. How long do you think that would take?"

"That's now entirely up to the American Embassy. It can take from a few days to several weeks or even months. We have no way of knowing that. But as of tonight, you are officially a guest of the United States of Mexico."

After yet another wild ride through the streets of Mexico City, the two-vehicle motorcade arrived at the small hotel that would become Lince's safe house. Sergio made a sharp turn from a narrow one-way street into a dark garage and brought the vehicle to a halt. The commander, who had followed them bumper-to-bumper, turned the VW Beetle around and left it parked at an angle to totally block the entrance to the garage.

Manuel and Lince stood by the van while Sergio walked out to the middle of the street holding the UZI in the open. With no direct access from the parking garage to the lobby, the men to walk outside before entering the hotel. Sergio signaled the others that all was clear.

The room booked by the FDS was at the end of the hallway on the fourth floor. The commander stepped in first and inspected every inch of the place, making sure that everything was in order. He said that he would return in the morning to bring Lince some toiletries and a spare change of clothes.

Sergio called room service and ordered eight glasses of rum and coke on ice, four for himself and four for Manuel. Ironically, Rum and cokes were called *Cuba Libres*—free Cubas. The agents placed their loaded weapons on top of the spare bed and pulled-out a deck of cards, engaging in what promised to be a very long game of poker. It was two forty-five in the morning on December 2nd, 1977.

Lince did not recall at what time he surrendered to the world of dreams. He woke up around ten the next morning to the smell of a fresh ham and cheese omelet, toast and coffee that his bodyguards had ordered from room service. He felt calm and rested, and was slowly coming to grips with the events that had transpired in the last twenty-four hours.

His thoughts wandered from his parents back in Havana, to his teammates at the competition site in Tequesquitengo, to Mendez and the Cuban Embassy agents who were probably still looking for him. His decisive, split-second action at the store in Mexico City had changed his life forever. Now he hoped to get on a flight soon to the United States and freedom.

Commander Vasquez showed up around nine o'clock with another team of bodyguards that would relieve Sergio and Manuel from duty.

"The Cubans have been scouting every foreign embassy in Mexico City looking for you," Vasquez told him. "I don't think they know yet that you went to the Americans. Maybe they are still waiting for you to call Duvalón."

Vasquez' words had just confirmed to him he had been right about the Duvalón's sham. The American Embassy must have briefed the Mexican government on the details of his defection, including the phone number and coded message that the stranger had given him back in Havana. By now, the Mexican Secret Service would know exactly where Duvalón's number would ring at, and if such a person actually existed. Vasquez, however, did not elaborate on the subject.

"Any word yet on when I will be leaving for the United States?"

"Nothing yet. You can rest assured, however, that the Mexican government is exerting a great deal of pressure on the American Embassy to put you on a flight to the United States. They would like to see you out of their hair as quickly as possible."

THE LYNX

Chapter 36

A thunderous round of applause broke out in the dining hall at the resort of Oaxtepec where the event's official banquet was being held. Tomás Berriolo, the founder and director of the Pan American Skydiving Federation, had delivered his compulsory speech to the audience and then went on to make an unexpected announcement. [14]

"As of today, the Cuban team will continue in the event short of one participant," Berriolo told his audience.

Tomás did not elaborate on the reasons why one of the Cubans was missing, nor did he give the man's name. It was not necessary. The news of Lince's escape had already reached the ears of every single participant in the competition.

Almost everyone present at the banquet hall joined in the outburst of joy, but for the dozen men and women seated at the Cuban delegation table. For the Cuban team this was a most humiliating moment. That night in Oaxtepec, parachutists from the free world had expressed solidarity with a fellow skydiver who had chosen freedom over personal glory.

---

[14] Page 335

When Berriolo finished his speech, the leader of the Cuban delegation walked up to the head table and pulled up a chair next to Berriolo.

"You have been a good friend of ours, Tomás. I trust you enough to tell you something in strict confidence," Mejias whispered.

"What would that be, *Señor* Mejias?"

"Our embassy believes that Nick had been sent by our government on a special mission."

Tomás turned in his chair to look at the man whose face was partially hidden by a huge Pancho Villa mustache. The director of the Pan American Games could hardly refrain from laughing.

"Sorry, *Señor* Mejias," It was not my intention to be impolite, but what you just said was really funny."

Stunned by Tomás' reaction, Mejias excused himself and returned to his table. His desperate attempt to draw suspicions on Nick following orders from the embassy had backfired and made him look stupid in the eyes of the competition's director. Only then he realized how ridiculous and desperate he must have sounded. What government on earth would send a secret agent on a mission overseas and then warn the enemy about it?

That morning in his office at the U.S. Interest Mission office in Havana, Lyle Lane struggled to get a grip on a situation that seemed to have gotten out of hand. In his job as chief negotiator for President Carter in Cuba, he felt compelled to do some damage control over an issue that, in his eyes, should have never been allowed to happen.

Lane believed that both Ambassador Lucey and Secretary of State Vance had made a big mistake by granting political asylum tithe Cuban defector. He viewed the decision as extremely inopportune, particularly at a time when the United States and Cuba were about to restore full diplomatic ties. His dreams of becoming the first U.S. ambassador to Cuba in sixteen years had just been shattered to pieces.

Lane had answered a phone call in the middle of the night at his residence in the elegant neighborhood of Cubanacán. The man at the other side of the line identified himself as a personal assistant to Raul Roa, Cuba's Minister of Foreign Affairs.

"Good morning, Mr. Lane. I apologize for calling you at such an odd time in the morning. However, our government has just learned that one of our athletes competing in Mexico was given refuge at the American Embassy in Mexico City."

"Minister Roa asked me to remind you that it is not standard policy of the United States to grant asylum to individuals at its embassies overseas," the aide continued. "Your country has broken protocol by giving refuge to an ex-member of the Cuban parachute team. How can we take your wishes to normalize diplomatic relationships with the Republic of Cuba seriously when you do things of this nature behind our backs? We demand the immediate return of the rogue parachutist to the Cuban authorities."

Lane could have told the Cuban government official on the phone that, under extreme circumstances, American embassies have jurisdiction to grant temporary refuge to a person when his or her life is in immediate danger. But he didn't. It would not be politically correct to further upset the Cuban Chancellor, or his intermediary.

Instead, Lane told Mr. Roa's emissary that it had been the U.S. Ambassador to Mexico, or perhaps other senior official at that embassy who made the decision to give Nickolich temporary protection from the Cuban agents pursuing him. He added that the situation was now out of the U.S. government's hands.

"I don't know if Mr. Roa is aware of this, but the Mexican government has already granted political asylum to the former member of your skydiving team."

Lane, however, promised Mr. Roa's envoy that, for the sake of the U.S.—Cuba relations, he would try to persuade the State Department to keep the news of the skydiver's defection away from the media as long as possible.[15]

That morning at his office on the Malecon littoral, Lane dictated an urgent telex to Cyrus Vance, the U.S. Secretary of State. The telex was transmitted to Washington at 7:49 a.m. and spoke volumes about where Lyle Lane's heart was on that fateful day.

---

[15] Page 351

0 031706Z DEC 77 FM USINT HAVANA

TO SECSTATE WASHDC NIACT IMMEDIATE 655 INFO AMEMBASSY MEXICO NIACT IMMEDIATE

S E C R E T HAVANA 0749 EO 11652: XGDS-4 TAGS: SREF CU

SUBJ: CUBAN ASYLUM REQUEST REF: MEXICO 20019

AT THIS EARLY AND CURRENTLY SENSITIVE STAGE OF A PROCESS OF "NORMALIZATION" OF RELATIONSHIPS WITH CUBA, IT SEEMS PARTICULARLY UNFORTUNATE FOR U.S. TO TAKE AN ACTION IN SUBJECT CASE WHICH IS NOT CONSISTENT WITH ACTIONS WE WOULD ROUTINELY TAKE IN SUCH MATTERS AT ANY OTHER TIME. WE WOULD PRESUMABLY TAKE THE FULL ONUS FOR THIS ACTION WITH THE GOVERNMENT OF CUBA FOR THE SAKE OF OUR RELATIONS WITH MEXICO.

(PARAGRAPH EXCISED BY STATE DEP.)

IN ANY CASE, WE HOPE THAT EVERY EFFORT WILL BE MADE BY ALL PARTIES CONCERNED TO AVOID PUBLICITY IN THIS CASE. ANY PRESS ATTENTION WOULD, OF COURSE, FURTHER EMBARRASS THE CUBAN GOVERNMENT AND THUS COMPLICATE OUR RELATIONS EVEN MORE.

LANE

THE LYNX

Chapter 37

Lince awoke to a subtle knocking on the door. He glanced at the luminous dial of his Junghans watch and noticed it was two-fifteen in the morning.

Sergio had positioned himself behind the bed with his UZI aimed at the door. Meanwhile, Manuel attached the door security chain and opened the door a crack while holding his .45 pistol with the other hand. Sergio and Manuel must have relieved the second team of bodyguards while he slept.

After checking the visitors' IDs, Manuel released the door chain and allowed the men to step inside. One of them introduced himself to Lince as the first secretary of the American Embassy in Mexico City.

"Nick, I have good news for you. You are leaving for Miami on an Aeromexico flight first thing tomorrow morning."

"Thank you, sir. That's the best news I've ever had in my life."

The man handed him an envelope. "Here is your airline ticket and the pre-parole document that will allow you to enter the

United States. You won't need a passport."

The secretary took out his wallet and pulled out a fifty-dollar bill.

"You can use the money to contact your family once you arrive in Florida. Have a safe flight and good luck to you in your new life."

At daybreak, Secret Service agent Sergio Temimipa drove the VW van once again at high-speed through the streets of Mexico City and then on the highway to the airport. He flashed his ID to a guard at one of the airport's side gates and parked the van in an area reserved for official vehicles. Sergio and Manuel proceeded to escort Lince through an inner terminal corridor and into a small office where a Mexican immigration official was waiting for their arrival. The time had come to complete one last formality between the Cuban defector and the Mexican government.

"*Señor* Nickolich, there is one last document for you to sign. It states that you are declining the political asylum granted to you by the government of Mexico."

Lince glanced over the document and promptly signed his name at the bottom. He thanked the Mexican immigration official for his government's kind hospitality and for giving him protection.

"We need to find your gate now," Sergio told him. "You don't want to miss your flight."

"I'll be praying that your airplane doesn't get hijacked to Cuba," Manuel joked. All three men laughed.

Lince left Mexico City for Miami on Aeromexico Flight 410 on the morning of December 3, 1977, less than seventy-two hours after seizing a momentous opportunity to break free from his captors and change his destiny forever.

Epilogue

At eight in the morning on December 5, 1977, a military truck pulled into the driveway at the house numbered 1708 on 174th Street in Siboney, an upscale neighborhood in western Havana.

A detail of eight armed operatives jumped off the truck bed and secured both the front door and the side door next to the two-car garage. The leader of the raid team attempted to open the front door, but found it locked. He then rang the bell and started banging on the glass panel while yelling:

"State Security, open at once."

Moments later, a frail-looking lady in her late sixties started down the stairs slowly with a dignified posture.

"Hurry up," yelled the man outside.

Ramona didn't rush. Without altering her pace, she made it down to the marble stairwell landing and unlocked the glass door.

"I know why you are here. My son is now a free man. He just called us from the United States. There is nothing you can do to him now."

In what resembled a well-rehearsed military maneuver, six DSE operatives took off running up the spiral stairway, while one stayed outside guarding the door. The man who acted as the leader put his hand on Ramona's back and tried to push her up the stairs.

"Keep your hands off me," she demanded. "I don't need your help."

"Where is your son's bedroom?"

"Down the hallway, second door on the left."

Moments later, Victor Daniels, who had turned eighty-three years old, was led to his own dining room by one of the soldiers and prompted to sit at the table next to his wife. He was still in his pajamas and his eyes were wide open with fear. Ramona remained calm with a proud look etched in her bright-green eyes.

"Neither of you can get up from this table while we search the house. If you need to use the bathroom, one of us will have to accompany you."

Ramona looked at the soldier with a spiteful look in her eyes. She wanted to tell him everything she had held inside for the past eighteen years—the long and harsh years of suffering lived under Castro's tyrannical regime. Anticipating what his wife was about to do, Victor Daniels put his hand on her shoulder and implored her with his eyes to remain silent.

The last time something like that happened to them was when a militiaman named Martinez and two others had ransacked the house searching for weapons back in 1961. This time it was much worse.

The G2 agents virtually turned the house upside down, moving from room to room with military precision. They dug inside closets and drawers, throwing into several large cardboard boxes everything that had belonged to Nick—his trophies, medals, toys, articles of clothing, books, his Zenith radio—everything.

Ramona noticed one of the men walking downstairs with a large picture book.

"You can't take that. That's our family album."

"We can take everything we think is necessary for our investigation," one of the men told her. "Please remain quiet or both of you will get in serious trouble."

"I don't care about your threats," Ramona told the man. "You are nothing but a slave of the regime, one more sheep in the herd. Do whatever your bosses ordered you and then leave my house."

"None of you are welcome here," she added. "You can take away the material things that belonged to my son, but you will never take away our memories of him."

The police raid took almost two hours to complete. When the last soldier had gone out the door, the elderly couple walked up to the lookout on top of the stairwell. Piled in the back of the green army truck they saw twenty-six years worth of their son's life heading to only God knew where.

In the fall of 1978, Victor Daniels and Ramona received permission from the Cuban government to immigrate to the Unites States. Throughout that year, several officials from the

U.S. Interest Mission in Havana visited their home regularly. They believed those visits had prevented further abuses by the regime. However, the couple was ordered not to sell, or give away anything in their home. All their belongings had been carefully inventoried by the secret police to the last piece of silverware and were now the pillaged property of the Cuban government.

Fortunately for Lince's parents, they had many friends who went to the house and checked on them from time to time. One of them was Pepín Fernandez, Lince's free diving friend. Pepín would invariably show up at the house once or twice a month with a freshly speared fish for Lince's mom to bake in the kitchen oven.

Victor Daniels and Ramona left for the United States via

Jamaica carrying only one small suitcase, each containing one change of clothes. They didn't look back, or minded leaving behind the fruits of a lifetime. They were happy to soon be reunited with their children and to meet their first grandchild, who was born two years earlier in freedom.

Their twenty-year-long nightmare was finally over.

A few months later, Pepín Fernandez was observed spearfishing from a row boat anchored on a reef a mile or so off the coast of Santa Fé. The people from the small town west of Havana had watched Pepín fishing there many times before and didn't think anything of it. At any rate, he was the national champion and one of the few divers in Cuba granted the privilege to use a boat to train for international competitions.

On that day Pepín had a different plan. He was waiting for his seven-month pregnant wife to swim from shore to the boat to begin their journey to freedom.

In 1995, his skydiving life would come full circle in the skies high above Lake Wales, Florida. On that day, Lince and Jerry Bird flew next to each other on an amazing 213 way free fall formation attempt to break the world skydiving record.

Twenty one years earlier, it was Jerry who gave Lince his first relative work lesson at the World Parachuting Championships in Szolnok, Hungary.

Fidel Castro continued to play along with Jimmy Carter's attempt to normalize relations with Cuba, but only on his own terms. The Cuban dictator would systematically reject Carter's demands to address human rights issues, compensate Americans for expropriated properties, reduce the scope of his relationship with the Soviet Union or, allow the slightest hint of democracy to flourish on the island. To the unrepentant Castro, those demands were unacceptable since they threatened the very core of his authoritarian powers.

As it was, the United States of America would have to remain the Cuban regime's greatest and most irreconcilable enemy for decades to come.

THE LYNX

Appendix I

A letter written by a U.S. Army Golden Knight to Lince's sister after the Pan American Skydiving Championships in Peru, 1975.

7 April, 1975

Dear Mrs. Leeder:

My name is Jack Brake and I recently met your brother Victor. We were both competing at the Pan American Parachuting Championships in Lima, Peru.

Victor said that it would be very bad for you and him to communicate directly so he asked me to write you. He sends you all his love and that he misses you very much. He would like to communicate with you, but that would be very bad. He also said not to mention that you had heard from him in your letters to anyone.

Please write me back and let me know how you are doing. I would be happy to relay your message to Victor when I see him again.

Thanks,

Jack Brake

U.S. Army Parachute Team
Ft. Bragg, NC

Excerpts from a letter sent to Lince by Captain Fred O'Donnell, team leader of the U.S. Army Parachute Team, 1977 Pan-American Champions.

2 March, 1978

Dear Victor:

I must apologize for not having written sooner, but we are currently very involved attempting to recapture the world parachuting records. We recently lost most of them to the USSR, all, in fact, except the night 10 men. The prospects look very good for us at this time, but only time will tell.

It is very difficult for an American to understand or appreciate all that you have gone through to gain your freedom. The many things we have in America, we often take for granted and fail to realize how many people have or will give their lives for that freedom.

I am truly grateful that I was able to help in some small way. It is not often that one can play a part in such a dramatic story.

Fred

Testimonial letter from Matt O'Gwynn, Member of the U.S. Army Parachute Team to Mexico, 1977.

This rambling remembrance is offered so the readers will better understand who we are, what we are, and most importantly why we are.

In November 1977, I was completing my first season on the United States Parachute Team Golden Knights. As a competition parachutist, I was attending my first international competition, the Pan American Parachuting Championships in Tequesquitengo, Morelos, Mexico. After a two-day flight in an Army YC-7A Caribou, we arrived in Mexico City and were transported to the hotel, our initial marshaling point. To say the least, this was a very exciting journey for a young soldier/ competitor. Even more intriguing, we were told to expect the team from Cuba. They had performed well at the previous Pan Am competition in Peru in 1975 and I was particularly fascinated with the idea of competing with these Soviet- backed jumpers.

My father spent 33 years in the U.S. Air Force, mainly with Strategic Air Command as a KC-97 tanker pilot. I vividly remember the Cuban Missile Crisis as the seven-year-old "man of the house". Dad was pulling alert in Alaska, Mom and I were at home on Dover AFB in Delaware with plans to stay in the basement for approximately three weeks following the imminent nuclear conflict.

In Tequesquitengo, I was introduced to Victor Nickolich, who held the title of Master of Sport in Cuba. Having competed against my team leader in 1975 in Peru, Nick was well known and well respected. In a conversation, Nick mentioned being grounded and out of the sport for a full year for having fraternized with members of my team in Peru.

Midway through the competition, we were treated to a day off and a trip to Cuernavaca for sightseeing and shopping. When I entered the dining hall that evening, I knew immediately something was up. A very subtle air of tension permeated the room. Teams huddled and spoke quietly over dinner. That's when Tomas Berriolo, the meet director, announced that the Cubans would be continuing the meet minus one competitor. When I asked what was going on, my team leader and head of delegation, both gave me a look that I would understand later on. For the present moment I was clueless. At some point during that day, Nick disappeared. As I sat on the bus the following morning and we twisted and turned around each curve on the road, it finally sank in: Nick had made his move to freedom.

No official word was given until we landed in Harlingen, Texas on the flight home. Once back in our country, our team leader broke the news that Nick was safe in the U.S. The following May, 1978, he came up from Miami to a competition at Raeford, NC, our home DZ just a mile off of Fort Bragg. Each of us hugged our brother, glad beyond words for his victory.

Anyone who has pursued a passion knows how hard it is to 'move on' to the next phase of life. Leaving behind the thrill of competing, the adrenaline, and the camaraderie is something I also dealt with, albeit not in the most productive manner. During my three-decade-long break from classic Style and Accuracy competition, not a day went by without my longing to return. Last week at Lake Wales, FL., I managed to place 4th Overall of all competitors and earned, once again, a place on the United States Parachute Team. Words do not describe my respect for athletes who overcome obstacles, which we Americans will never experience in any part of our lives.

Matt O'Gwynn

1977 U.S. Army Parachute Team

Appendix II

Testimonials

Copies of the secret telexes (declassified) dated from December 1–3, 1977, and exchanged between the U.S. Department of State, the American Embassy in Mexico City, and the U.S. Special Interest Mission in Havana pertaining the defection of the Cuban skydiver in Mexico.

The documents were released to the author under the Freedom of Information Act.

Case Number: 200601114

SECRET

UNCLASSIFIED

PAGE 01   MEXICO 20019   020202Z
ACTION ARA-14

INFO OCT-01 ISO-00 SS-15 NSCE-00 L-03 HA-05 PRS-01
      CA-01 VO-05 CIAE-00 INR-07 NSAE-00 INRE-00 DODE-00
      FBIE-00 SY-05 INSE-00 SSO-00 (ISO) W
      ------------------027570 020451Z /63

O 020150Z DEC 77
FM AMEMBASSY MEXICO
TO SECSTATE WASHDC NIACT IMMEDIATE 6689

S E C R E T MEXICO 20019

EO 11652: XGDS4
TAGS: SREF, CU
SUBJECT: CUBAN ASYLUM REQUEST

Dept. of State, RPS/IPS, Margaret P. Grafeld, Dir.
( ) Release (✓) Excise ( ) Deny ( ) Declassify
Date 3/28/07 Exemption b1

REF: 2FAM 229.3

1. AFTERNOON DECEMBER 1, CUBAN NATIONAL CAME TO EMBASSY
REQUESTING ASYLUM. FOLLOWING INFO AS REQUESTED 2 FAM
228.5:

A. VICTOR NICKOLICH   CUBAN

B. MARCH 13, 1951, HAVANA, TRANSLATOR INTO ENGLISH.
(COMMENT: NICKOLICH IS MEMBER OF CUBAN CIVILIAN PARACHUTE
TEAM PARTICIPATING IN MEXICAN SPONSORED INTERNATIONAL
PARACHUTE COMPETITION. HE STATES HE IS A CIVILIAN.)

C. HOLDS CREDENTIAL AUTHORIZING HIS PARTICIPATION
IN PARACHUTE GAMES IN MEXICO.

D. SINCE NICKOLICH LEFT HIS TEAM COLLEAGUES SOME-
TIME MORNING DEC 1 IT SEEMS CERTAIN CUBAN EMBASSY KNOWS
OR SUSPECTS HE HAS FLED. DCM HAS NOTIFIED UNDERSECRETARY
OF FOREIGN RELATIONS OF MEXICO, AS WILL BE REPORTED BELOW.
    SECRET

    SECRET

PAGE 02   MEXICO 20019   020202Z

Current Class: SECRET

Dept. of State, RPS/IPS, Margaret P. Grafeld, Dir. Page: 2
( ) Classify as (✓) Extend as (≤) Downgrade to ___
Date 9/5/06 Declassify on 1/4/2031 Reason 25x1

Case Number: 200601114

E.   SUBJECT WALKED INTO EMBASSY REQUESTING ASYLUM.

F.   HE HAS BEEN AFFORDED TEMPORARY REFUGE IN EMBASSY.

G.   HE STATES HE WISHES TO LIVE IN A FREE SOCIETY.
NICKOLICH STATES HE HAS U.S. CITIZEN SISTER, MRS. VICTORIA
MILITZA PADILLA, BORN 12/30/48 IN HAVANA, ADDRESS UNKNOWN,
TELEPHONE NUMBER 552-8210 IN MIAMI. HE SAYS IF SISTER IS
NO LONGER AT THIS NUMBER, SHE CAN BE REACHED THROUGH
COUSIN, DOLORES FRONTELA, TELEPHONES 883-2041 OR 887-7505,
BOTH ALSO IN MIAMI.

    H. NO KNOWN CRIMINAL CHARGES

    I. STATES HE IS NOT COMMUNIST PARTY AFFILIATE.

2   Excised

                         DCM CONTACTED UNDER-
SECRETARY ALFONSO ROSENZWEIG-DIAZ, TO INFORM HIM OF CASE
AND REQUEST THAT GOM ACCEPT NICKOLICH AS ASYLEE IN MEXICO.
ROSENZWEIG-DIAZ AGREED THAT MEXICO SHOULD AND NORMALLY
WOULD ACCEPT HIM, BUT POINTED OUT THAT IT WOULD BE EX-
TREMELY EMBARRASSING FOR GOM TO HAVE HIM ON ITS HANDS
WITH FOREIGN SECRETARY ROEL DUE TO LEAVE DECEMBER 5 FOR
OFFICIAL VISIT TO CUBA. HE ASKED WHETHER USG COULD CON-
TINUE HIM IN TEMPORARY REFUGEE STATUS IN EMBASSY OR
ARRANGE FOR HIS TRAVEL TO U.S. DCM COUNTERED WITH SUG-
GESTION THAT GOM TAKE CHARGE OF HIM BUT KEEP HIM UNDER
WRAPS UNTIL ROEL VISIT OVER, AND UNDERSECRETARY SAID HE
    SECRET

    SECRET

PAGE 03   MEXICO 20019   020202Z

WOULD CONSIDER THIS, BUT DOUBTED HE WOULD BE SUCCESSFUL
IN GETTING SUCH ACTION APPROVED. ROSENZWEIG-DIAZ SUB-
SEQUENTLY OFFERED TO HAVE MEXICAN IMMIGRATION TAKE CHARGE
OF SUBJECT PENDING A U.S. DECISION ON ACCEPTING
HIM FOR IMMIGRATION. HE GAVE FIRM ASSURANCES, IN RE-
SPONSE TO SPECIFIC QUESTION BY DCM, THAT GOM WOULD NOT
TURN HIM OVER TO CUBAN AUTHORITIES AND ALSO THAT GOM
WOULD TAKE FULL SECURITY MEASURES TO ENSURE THAT NICKOLICH
WAS PROTECTED AGAINST ANY POSSIBLE KIDNAP ATTEMPT WHILE
IN GOM HANDS.

Case Number: 200601114

3. ACTION: REQUEST IMMEDIATE AUTHORIZATION TO PRE-
PAROLE NICKOLICH INTO U.S. ON URGENT BASIS. WE RECOG-
NIZE THAT TO DO SO COULD COMPLICATE U.S.-CUBAN RELATIONS.
HOWEVER, IT IS IMPORTANT TO U.S.-MEXICAN RELATIONS THAT
WE COOPERATE IN RELIEVING GOM OF EMBARRASSING DIFFICULTY
OUR FAILURE TO ACT WOULD CREATE FOR MEXICAN AUTHORITIES.
LUCEY

   SECRET

NNN

Current Class: SECRET   Page: 1
Current Handling: n/a
  Document Number: 1977STATE287794   Channel: n/a

UNCLASSIFIED

SECRET

PAGE 01   STATE 287794
ORIGIN SS-15

INFO   OCT-01   ARA-10   ISO-00   HA-05   NSCE-00   L-03   PRS-01
       CA-01   VO-05   CIAE-00   INR-07   NSAE-00   INRE-00   DODE-00
       FBIE-00   SY-05   INSE-00   SSO-00   /053 R

DRAFTED BY S/S:KSMITH:WES
APPROVED BY S/S:LFLEISCHER
ARA/CCA:ADBOWEN
ARA/MEX:HBLANE
HA/ORM:LARTHUR
                    ------------------027291 020410Z /64
O 020351Z DEC 77 ZFF4
FM SECSTATE WASHDC
TO AMEMBASSY MEXICO NIACT IMMEDIATE

S E C R E T STATE 287794

E.O. 11652: XGDS-4

TAGS:SREF, CU

SUBJECT: CUBAN ASYLUM REQUEST

REF: MEXICO 20019

DEPARTMENT REVIEWING REQUEST FOR ADMISSION OF NICKOLICH
TO US. WE EXPECT TO SEND FURTHER GUIDANCE TOMORROW.   VANCE

     SECRET

NNN

UNCLASSIFIED

Current Class: SECRET   UNCLASSIFIED   Page:

Current Class: SECRET
Current Handling: STADIS
Document Number: 1977STATE288198

UNCLASSIFIED

Page: 1

Channel: n/a

UNCLASSIFIED

PAGE 01   STATE   288198
ORIGIN HA-05

INFO OCT-01 ARA-10 ISO-00 SS-15 L-03 VO-05 CA-01
      INR-07 PRS-01 SY-05 SSO-00 INRE-00 /053 R

DRAFTED BY HA:ORM:LARTHUR:CAF
APPROVED BY HA:JLCARLIN
HA/ORM - SCLOWMAN
ARA - WSTEDMAN
ARA/CCA - DBOWEN
                        ------------------036847 022121Z /61

O 022101Z DEC 77
FM SECSTATE WASHDC
TO AMEMBASSY MEXICO IMMEDIATE

S E C R E T STATE 288198

UNCLASSIFIED

STADIS////////////////////

E.O. 11652: XGDS-4

TAGS: SREF, CU VICTOR NICKOLICH

SUBJECT: CUBAN ASYLUM SEEKER

REF: MEXICO 20019
1. INS/CO HAS BEEN CONSULTED CONCERNING THIS CASE.

Excised

UNCLASSIFIED

PAGE 02   STATE   288198

2. IN ANY EVENT, SUBJECT SHOULD BE TURNED OVER PROMPTLY TO
MEXICAN AUTHORITIES RATHER THAN REMAIN IN EMBASSY WHILE

Current Class: SECRET

UNCLASSIFIED

Current Class: SECRET
Current Handling: STADIS
Document Number: 1977STATE288198

HIS REQUEST FOR ADMISSION INTO U.S. IS PURSUED.
3. FYI - MIAMI TELEPHONE NUMBER FOR SUBJECT'S SISTER
HAS BEEN DISCONNECTED. SUBJECT'S COUSIN HAS BEEN ASKED
TO HAVE MRS. PADILLA IMMEDIATELY CONTACT DEPT. SO THAT
SPECIAL APPOINTMENT CAN BE ARRANGED WITH INS/MIAMI. END
FYI.

4. THE EMBASSY MAY USE THE FOLLOWING PRESS GUIDANCE
STRICTLY ON AN IF ASKED BASIS:
Q. CAN YOU TELL US ANYTHING ABOUT A CUBAN WHO MAY HAVE
RECENTLY CONTACTED THE EMBASSY SEEKING ENTRY INTO THE
U.S.?

A. A CUBAN DID CONTACT THE EMBASSY SEEKING TO IMMIGRATE
TO THE U.S. HE INFORMED US THAT HE HAS RELATIVES WHO
ARE U.S. CITIZENS AND HE IS ATTEMPTING TO OBTAIN AN
IMMIGRANT VISA.

Q. CAN YOU TELL US HIS NAME AND OCCUPATION?

A. I AM SORRY BUT FOR PRIVACY CONSIDERATION, I CANNOT
DIVULGE THAT INFORMATION.

Q. DID THE INDIVIDUAL MAKE A REQUEST FOR ASYLUM IN THE
U.S.?

A. A BASIC TENET OF U.S. GOVERNMENT POLICY REGARDING SUCH
MATTERS IS TO MAINTAIN THE CONFIDENTIALITY OF INDIVIDUAL
ASYLUM REQUESTS. I, THEREFORE, CANNOT ANSWER THAT QUESTION.

SECRET

SECRET

PAGE 03   STATE 288198

HOWEVER, I WOULD LIKE TO POINT OUT THAT HE DOES HAVE U.S.
CITIZEN RELATIVES AND HE IS ACTIVELY PURSUING AN IMMIGRANT
VISA FOR ENTRY INTO THE U.S.

Q. WAS HE ALLOWED TO REMAIN IN THE EMBASSY LAST NIGHT,
AND IF SO, IS THIS THE USUAL PROCEDURE IN IV CASES?

A. WHILE SOMEWHAT UNUSUAL, HE WAS ALLOWED TO REMAIN IN
THE EMBASSY OVERNIGHT FOR SOME 24 HOURS.   VANCE

SECRET

NNN

UNCLASSIFIED
SECRET

DOC_NBR:	1977HAVANA00749
FILM:	D770449-0521
DATE:	03 DEC 1977
TYPE:	TE
FROM:	HAVANA
DRAFTER:	n/a
OFFICE:	ACTION ARA
TO:	STATE
CHANNEL:	n/a
ORIGHAND:	n/a
ORIGPHAND:	n/a
ORIGCLASS:	SECRET
ORIGPCLASS:	n/a
EO:	X4
SUBJECT:	CUBAN ASYLUM REQUEST
REFERENCE:	77 MEXICO 20019
CONTROL_NBR:	n/a
ENCLOSURE:	n/a
LOCATOR:	TEXT ON-LINE, ON MICROFILM
ERRORS:	N/A
CONCEPTS:	REFUGEES
TAGS:	SREF, CU

UNCLASSIFIED

UNCLASSIFIED
SECRET

PAGE 01   HAVANA 00749 032259Z
ACTION ARA-14

INFO OCT-01 ISO-00 SS-15 NSCE-00 L-03 HA-05 PRS-01
      CA-01 VO-05 CIAE-00 INR-07 NSAE-00 INRE-00 DODE-00
      FBIE-00 SY-05 INSE-00 SSO-00 /057 W
      --------------------049401 032353Z /72

O 031706Z DEC 77
FM USINT HAVANA
TO SECSTATE WASHDC NIACT IMMEDIATE 655
INFO AMEMBASSY MEXICO NIACT IMMEDIATE

S E C R E T HAVANA 0749

EO 11652: XGDS-4
TAGS: SREF CU
SUBJ: CUBAN ASYLUM REQUEST

REF: MEXICO 20019

AT THIS EARLY AND CURRENTLY SENSITIVE STAGE OF A PROCESS OF
"NORMALIZATION" OF RELATIONS WITH CUBA, IT SEEMS PARTICULARLY
UNFORTUNATE FOR U.S. TO TAKE AN ACTION IN SUBJECT CASE WHICH IS
NOT CONSISTENT WITH ACTIONS WE WOULD ROUTINELY TAKE IN SUCH MATTERS
AT ANY OTHER TIME. WE WOULD PRESUMABLY TAKE THE FULL ONUS FOR THIS

UNCLASSIFIED

ACTION WITH GOC FOR THE SAKE OF OUR RELATIONS WITH MEXICO.

Excised

2. IN ANY CASE, WE HOPE THAT EVERY EFFORT WILL BE MADE BY ALL
PARTIES CONCERNED TO AVOID PUBLICITY IN THIS CASE. ANY PRESS
ATTENTION WOULD, OF COURSE, FURTHER EMBARRASS THE CUBAN GOVERN-
MENT AND THUS COMPLICATE OUR RELATIONS EVEN MORE.
LANE

SECRET

NNN

SECRET

THE LYNX